TREASURY OF LITERATURE—READTEXT SERIES

MAGIC CARPET

New Enlarged Edition

Selected and Edited by
ELEANOR M. JOHNSON
Editor-in-Chief
My Weekly Reader
and
LELAND B. JACOBS
Professor of Education
Teachers College, Columbia University
Specialist in Children's Literature

CHARLES E. MERRILL BOOKS, INC.
Columbus, Ohio

TREASURY OF LITERATURE

Readtext Series

The books in this series are:

MERRY-GO-ROUND
•
HAPPINESS HILL
••
TREAT SHOP
•••
MAGIC CARPET
••••
ENCHANTED ISLES
•••••
ADVENTURE LANDS
••••••

CHARLES E. MERRILL BOOKS, INC.

1300 Alum Creek Drive · Columbus 16, Ohio

© Copyright 1960, 1954, by Charles E. Merrill Books, Inc. and Artists and Writers Press, Inc. Printed in the U.S.A. by Western Printing and Lithographing Company. Published simultaneously in Canada by Thomas Nelson & Sons (Canada) Limited.

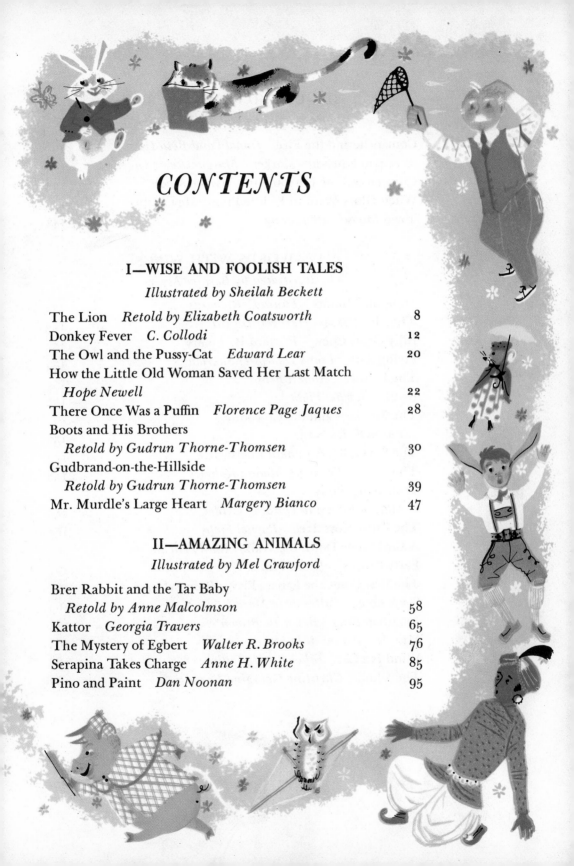

CONTENTS

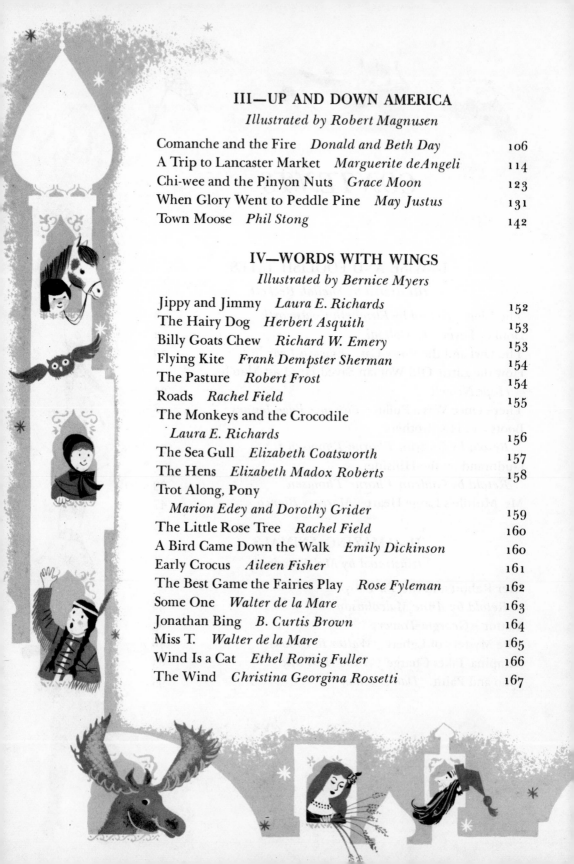

III—UP AND DOWN AMERICA

Illustrated by Robert Magnusen

IV—WORDS WITH WINGS

Illustrated by Bernice Myers

V—STRONG MAGIC

Illustrated by Bernice Myers

VI—WHEN OUR COUNTRY WAS YOUNGER

Illustrated by John Moment

VII—TALES THAT GREW TALL
Illustrated by George Wilde

VIII—IT COULD HAPPEN TO YOU
Illustrated by Violet Lamont

IX—THERE WAS A TIME
Illustrated by Robert Magnusen

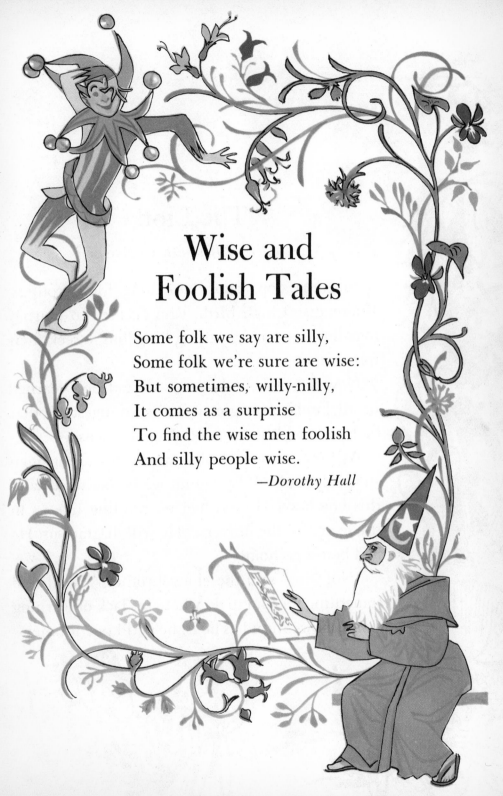

Wise and
Foolish Tales

Some folk we say are silly,
Some folk we're sure are wise:
But sometimes, willy-nilly,
It comes as a surprise
To find the wise men foolish
And silly people wise.

—*Dorothy Hall*

The Lion

Retold by Elizabeth Coatsworth

In India, long ago, there were four brothers, Brahmans of high birth, who decided to journey together into a neighboring kingdom to seek their fortunes.

Now three of the brothers were deeply learned in all kinds of magic. But the youngest brother had nothing but his good common sense.

As they journeyed on, one of the young men suddenly said, "Why should we be bothered with this boy here? He has had no training like us in the secrets of the universe. He will disgrace us. He had better go home."

"No! No!" said the eldest brother. "We'll find something for him to do where his lack of learning won't show. Stupid as he is, he's still our brother."

So they journeyed on. After a while they came
to a jungle. In the path, they saw a heap of old
bones. They stopped to look.

The boy was first to see what the bones were.
"It was a lion," he said, turning to go on.

But the proud brother stopped him. "Wait a
minute," he said. "I'll show you something to make
you open wide your stupid eyes. See, with a few
words I can call these bones together."

He spoke the words of power. And, as he spoke,
the dry bones clattered together. In a moment,
there in the path before them stood the skeleton
of the lion on its skeleton paws. The green of the
jungle showed through its white, chalky ribs.

Then the youngest brother was surprised indeed.
"Let us go on," he cried. "I do not like skeletons
which stand up and look at you without eyes."

"Why, you must be a coward as well as a fool,"
said the second brother, laughing. "Wait a moment. I will show you a trick to match his!" He,
too, spoke a charm. And before their staring eyes
the skeleton turned into a lion with flesh as well
as bones, and a tawny coat, and a great mane, and
eyes yellow as amber.

The youngest brother looked very uneasy. "Do come now," he begged the others. "It is getting late. We still have far to go."

But when anyone has started a thing, it is hard to put it aside not quite finished. Besides, the

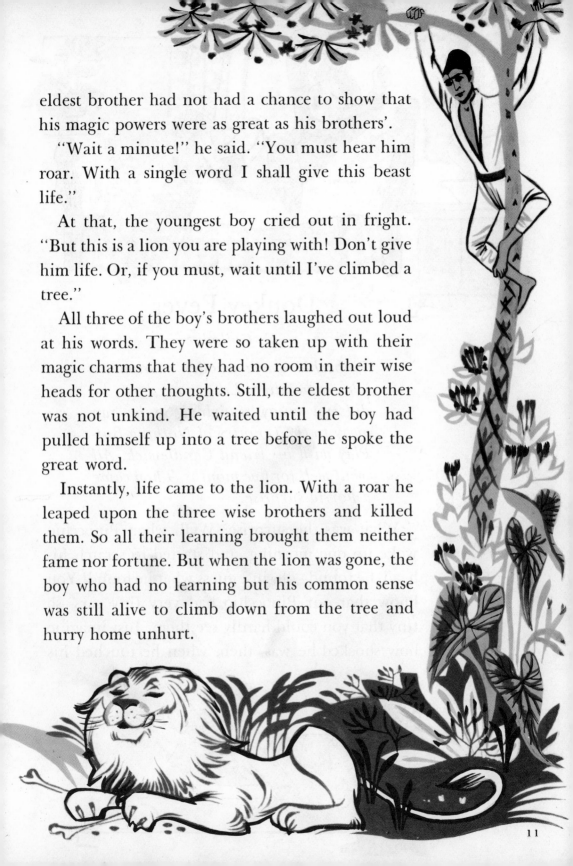

eldest brother had not had a chance to show that his magic powers were as great as his brothers'.

"Wait a minute!" he said. "You must hear him roar. With a single word I shall give this beast life."

At that, the youngest boy cried out in fright. "But this is a lion you are playing with! Don't give him life. Or, if you must, wait until I've climbed a tree."

All three of the boy's brothers laughed out loud at his words. They were so taken up with their magic charms that they had no room in their wise heads for other thoughts. Still, the eldest brother was not unkind. He waited until the boy had pulled himself up into a tree before he spoke the great word.

Instantly, life came to the lion. With a roar he leaped upon the three wise brothers and killed them. So all their learning brought them neither fame nor fortune. But when the lion was gone, the boy who had no learning but his common sense was still alive to climb down from the tree and hurry home unhurt.

Donkey Fever

C. Collodi

Pinocchio was a wooden marionette who came alive. Like many boys, he did not enjoy studying. So he ran away to the Country of Nothing-But-Play with his friend Candlewick. All went well for five months. Then came a horrid surprise.

What was the surprise? Well, when Pinocchio woke up one morning, and started to scratch his head, he found—oh, just guess what he found! You know that our Pinocchio had very tiny ears—so tiny that you could hardly see them. Just imagine how shocked he was, then, when he touched his

head and found that his ears had grown until they seemed a foot long! He rushed to find a mirror, but he couldn't find one, so he poured some water into a washbowl instead. And there in the water he saw two long, magnificent donkey ears!

Oh, how sorrowful and ashamed our poor Pinocchio felt! He sobbed in despair. He screamed. He knocked his head against the wall. But the harder he cried the more his ears grew—and grew —and grew. Hair began to sprout on their tips.

Hearing his heart-rending cries, a Dormouse who lived on the first floor hurried into the room. Seeing the marionette in such a state, she asked anxiously, "What is the matter with you, my dear little fellow-lodger?"

"Oh, Mrs. Dormouse, I'm very sick and it frightens me. Do you know how to count a pulse?"

"Perhaps."

"Then see if I have a fever."

The Dormouse took Pinocchio's wrist and held it in her paw. In a few moments she said, "My little friend, I'm sorry, but I have some bad news for you."

"What can it be?" cried Pinocchio.

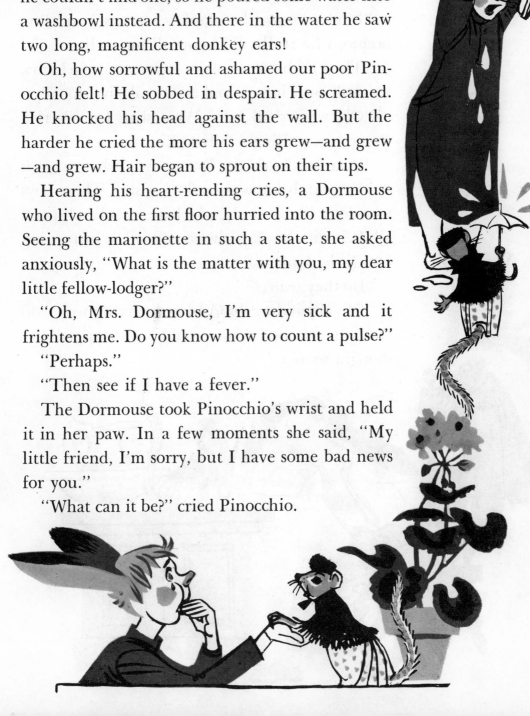

"You have a terrible fever," said the Dormouse.

"What kind of fever is it?"

"The donkey fever."

"I don't know what donkey fever is," said Pinocchio, who really did know all too well.

"Then I'd better explain. In two or three hours, you will turn into a donkey—a real, live donkey."

"Oh, what shall I do? What shall I do?" cried Pinocchio, pulling wildly at his ears.

"Dear boy," said the Dormouse, "what *can* you do? You surely know what the law says. Those boys who don't like to study, who hate school and spend all their time in play, always end at last by turning into little donkeys."

"Do they *really?*"

"Of course they do. And now, crying won't do you a bit of good. You should have stopped and thought sooner."

"Oh, but it wasn't my fault. Truly, it was all Candlewick's fault."

"And who may Candlewick be?"

"A boy I know. Oh, I wanted to go back to school. I wanted to get my lessons and make the good Fairy proud of me. But Candlewick told me, 'In the Country of Nothing-But-Play, *nobody* studies. We can just play all day long, from morning till night.'"

"And why did you listen to a good-for-nothing scamp like that?"

"Why? Oh, Mrs. Dormouse, because I am a stupid, ungrateful marionette. If I weren't such a worthless creature I never would have left my good Fairy, who did so much for me. And by this time I would have turned into a *real* little boy, like lots of other marionettes."

He started to go out the door, but remembered his donkey ears just in time. And being ashamed to have anyone see him, he made a cotton cap and put it on, pulling it way down over his ears. Then he set out to hunt for Candlewick.

But Candlewick did not seem to be around

anywhere. Pinocchio went up and down each street and to all the theaters—everywhere. At last he went to Candlewick's house and knocked.

"Who's there?" called Candlewick from inside.
"Pinocchio."
"Well, wait a minute. I'll open the door."

Companions in Misery

Pinocchio waited and waited. After a long time the door opened, and Pinocchio saw that his friend had on a cap too, pulled down over *his* ears. Pinocchio looked at that cap and felt a little better. "Candlewick is in trouble too," he thought. "I'll bet he has donkey fever, just like me."

But Pinocchio pretended not to notice anything. "How are you today, Candlewick?" he asked in the most cheerful tone in the world.

"As happy as a mouse in cheese."

"Cross your heart?"

"Why should I tell a fib?"

"Maybe I shouldn't ask—but why are you wearing that cap?"

"Oh, the doctor thought I'd better wear it. I hurt my knee. But Pinocchio, why are *you* wearing that great big cap?"

"Well, the doctor told me to. I hurt my toe, you see."

"Oh, poor Pinocchio!"

"Oh, poor Candlewick!"

Then for a long time the boys didn't say anything at all. At last Pinocchio sort of whispered, "Pull up your cap just a little, won't you?"

"Nothing doing! Will you?"

"Nothing doing! You see—well, one of my ears hurts pretty badly."

"One of mine does, too."

"Oh, it does? Which one?"

"Both. And you?"

"Both. Have we both got the same thing?"

"I'm afraid so."

"Do something for me, Candlewick!"

"Of course."

"Let me look at your ears."

"Well, all right. But let me see yours first."

"No. After you."

"All right, then," said the marionette. "Let's make a bargain."

"What bargain?"

"Let's both take off our caps at the same time."

"All right. I'm willing."

"Ready, then." And Pinocchio began to count, 'One—two—three!"

At "three," both boys pulled their caps off and threw them up to the ceiling. And then, realizing that the same dreadful thing had happened to both of them, they burst into shouts of laughter. They laughed until they were weak.

Suddenly Candlewick stopped laughing and staggered. Turning white, he cried, "Help me! Help me, Pinocchio!"

"What's the matter?"

"Oh, dear! I can't stand up any longer!"

"I can't either!" cried Pinocchio. And at that very moment, they fell on hands and knees, and began to run around the room on all fours. And as they were running, their arms turned into legs, their faces grew long, and their bodies became all hairy. What used to be hands were now hoofs. But the very worst moment of all for those wretched boys was when each one felt a tail whisking behind him. Sad and ashamed, they tried to speak. Instead of sobs and cries, however, the only sounds they could make were donkeys' brays—"Hee-haw!"

If you are worried about Pinocchio, you will be happy to know that he finally learned his lesson. Yes, after many adventures, he did get over his donkey fever. And he finally became, instead of a marionette, a real boy!

The Owl and the Pussy-Cat

The Owl and the Pussy-Cat went to sea
   In a beautiful pea-green boat,
They took some honey, and plenty of money
   Wrapped up in a five-pound note.
The Owl looked up to the stars above,
   And sang to a small guitar,
"O lovely Pussy, O Pussy, my love,
   What a beautiful Pussy you are,
      You are,
      You are!
   What a beautiful Pussy you are!"

Pussy said to the Owl, "You elegant fowl,
   How charmingly sweet you sing!
Oh! let us be married, too long we have tarried:
   But what shall we do for a ring?"
They sailed away, for a year and a day,
   To the land where the Bong-tree grows;
And there in a wood a Piggy-wig stood,
   With a ring at the end of his nose,
      His nose,
      His nose,
   With a ring at the end of his nose.

"Dear Pig, are you willing to sell for one shilling
   Your ring?" Said the Piggy, "I will."
So they took it away, and were married next day
   By the Turkey who lives on the hill.
They dined on mince and slices of quince,
   Which they ate with a runcible spoon;
And hand in hand, on the edge of the sand,
   They danced by the light of the moon,
      The moon,
      The moon,
   They danced by the light of the moon.

                —*Edward Lear*

How the Little Old Woman Saved Her Last Match

Hope Newell

When the Little Old Woman looked in her match box one morning, she saw that she had only one match left.

"Dear me," she sighed. "Tomorrow is market day. I cannot buy any more matches until then. I will not let my fire go out, for I must save this match to light my lamp tonight."

As she was eating her breakfast, she thought, "Since I must keep the fire going all day, I may as well use it. I will heat the flatirons and do my weekly ironing."

After the Little Old Woman had washed and dried her breakfast dishes, she made ready to do her ironing. She set the irons on the stove to heat. She laid the ironing board across the backs of two chairs. She fetched a soap box to stand on so she could reach the ironing board.

When the flatirons were hot, she brought out her basket of clothes and began to iron. After she had ironed a few pieces, she began to worry about the match.

"Suppose the match got broken," she thought. "I could not light my lamp tonight. I had better wrap it in a piece of cotton."

She set down her iron and plucked a piece of cotton out of the red chair cushion. She wrapped the match in the cotton so it would not get broken.

She laid it carefully in the box and went back to her ironing. After she had ironed a few more pieces, she began to worry about the match again.

"Suppose the match got damp," she thought. "I could not light my lamp tonight. I had better put it in a tin can."

The Little Old Woman set down her iron and went to fetch a tin can. She put the match in the tin can and put a cover on it so the match would not get damp. She put the can carefully on the mantelpiece and went back to her ironing.

But after she had ironed quite a few pieces, she began to worry about the match again.

"Maybe it is not a good match and will not light when I strike it," she thought. "Then I could not light my lamp tonight."

The more she thought about it, the more worried she was.

"Dear me," she thought, "I know the match will not get broken, for I have wrapped it in cotton. I know it will not get damp, for I have put it in a tin can. But how am I to know whether it will light when I strike it?"

She worried so much about the match that she

forgot to mind her ironing. For a long time, she did not iron a single piece. She just stood on the soap box wondering if the match would light.

Finally she said, "This is no way to act. If I go on worrying about the match, I shall never get my ironing finished. Maybe if I use my head, I shall find out what to do."

So the Little Old Woman tied a wet towel around her head and sat down with her finger against her nose and shut her eyes.

She had hardly used her head any time before she knew what to do.

"How silly I am," chuckled the Little Old Woman. "I should have known what to do without

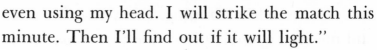

even using my head. I will strike the match this minute. Then I'll find out if it will light."

She took the match out of the tin can and unwrapped the cotton from it. Then she struck the match against the mantelpiece.

But it did not light.

She struck it again.

But the match did not light.

She struck it a third time, and the match burst into flame.

As she watched it burn, she said, "This match burns very nicely indeed."

When the match had burned out, the Little Old Woman went back to her ironing.

"Now I will not be worrying about the match," she thought. "I shall be able to mind my ironing."

She ironed and ironed, until by and by the basket was empty. Then she put her ironing board away and set her irons on the back of the stove to cool.

"It is getting dark now," she said to herself. "I had better light my lamp."

She filled the lamp with oil and trimmed the wick so that it would burn brightly.

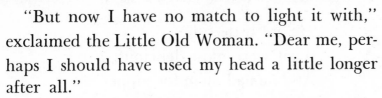

"But now I have no match to light it with," exclaimed the Little Old Woman. "Dear me, perhaps I should have used my head a little longer after all."

After she had thought about it a while, she said, "Oh, well, I can light a piece of paper from the fire in the stove. I can light the lamp from that."

When she had lighted the lamp with a piece of paper, she looked at the big pile of ironing she had done.

"It is just as well that I did strike the match to see if it would light," she said. "Otherwise, I would have worried all day, and I would never have finished so much ironing. I am a very clever Old Woman after all!"

There Once *Was a Puffin*

Oh, there once was a Puffin
Just the shape of a muffin,
And he lived on an island
In the
   bright
     blue
       sea!

He ate little fishes,
That were most delicious,
And he had them for supper
And he
   had
     them
       for tea.

But this poor little Puffin,
He couldn't play nothin',
For he hadn't anybody
To
   play
     with
       at all.

So he sat on his island,
And he cried for awhile, and
He felt very lonely,
And he
   felt
      very
         small.

Then along came the fishes,
And they said, "If you wishes,
You can have us for playmates,
Instead
   of
      for
         tea!"

So they now play together,
In all sorts of weather,
And the puffin eats pancakes,
Like you
   and
      like
         me.

                —*Florence Page Jaques*

Boots and His Brothers

Retold by Gudrun Thorne-Thomsen

Once upon a time, there was a man who had three sons—Peter, Paul, and Espen. Espen was called Boots. He was the youngest.

I can't say the man had anything except these three sons, for he did not possess one penny to rub against another. So he told his sons they must go out into the world to seek their fortune.

Now, a short way from the man's cottage was the King's palace. Just against the King's windows a great oak tree had sprung up. The oak was so stout and big that it took away all the light from the palace. The King had promised much gold to anyone who could fell the oak. But no one was man enough to do it. As soon as one chip of the oak's trunk flew off, two grew in its place.

The King wished also to have a well dug to hold water for a whole year. All his neighbors had wells, but he had none, and he thought that a shame. So the King said he would give to anyone who could dig him such a well both money and goods. But the King's palace lay high, high up on a hill. They could dig but a few inches before coming upon hard rock.

But the King had set his heart on having these two things done. He had it given out in all the churches that the man who could fell the big oak and dig him a well should have the Princess and half the kingdom.

Well! There was many a man who came to try his luck. But all their hacking and hewing, and all their digging and delving were useless.

One day, the three brothers thought they too would set off and try. Their father had not a word to say against it. Even if they did not get the

Princess and half the kingdom, it might happen they would get a place somewhere with a good master. So he consented at once. Peter, Paul, and Espen set forth.

They had not gone far before they came to a fir wood. At one side there rose a steep hill. As they went along, they heard something hewing and hacking away up on the hill.

"I wonder now what it is that is hewing away up yonder," said Boots.

"You're always so clever with your wondering," laughed Peter and Paul. "What wonder is it, pray, that a wood cutter should stand and hack up on a hillside?"

"Still, I'd like to see what it is, after all," said Boots. Up he went.

"Oh, if you're such a child, it will do you good to go and take a lesson," called out his brothers after him.

But Boots didn't care. He climbed the hillside towards the spot whence the noise came. When he reached the place, what do you think he saw? Why, an ax that stood there hacking and hewing, all of itself, at the trunk of a fir tree.

"Good-day," said Boots. "So you stand here all alone and hew, do you?"

"Yes, here I've stood and hewed for hundreds of years, waiting for you," said the ax.

"Well, here I am at last," said Boots. He took the ax, pulled it off its haft, and stuffed head and haft into his bag. When he got down again to his brothers, they began to jeer and laugh at him.

"And now, what strange thing was it up yonder on the hillside?" they asked.

"Oh, it was only an ax we heard," said Boots.

When they had gone on a bit farther, their road passed under a steep rock. There they heard something digging and shoveling.

"I wonder now," said Boots, "what is digging and shoveling up yonder at the top of the rock."

"Ah," laughed Peter and Paul again. "As if you'd never heard a woodpecker hacking and pecking at a hollow tree!"

"Well, well," said Boots, "I just think it would be fun to see what it really is."

So off he set to climb the rock. When he got near to the top, what do you think he saw? Why, a spade that stood there digging and delving.

"Good-day!" said Boots. "So you stand here all alone, and dig and delve, do you?"

"Yes, that's what I do," said the spade. "And that's what I've done these hundreds of years, waiting for you, Boots."

"Well, here I am," said Boots again. He took the spade and knocked it off the handle, and put it into his bag. Then he returned to his brothers.

"Well, what was it, so rare and strange," said Peter and Paul, "that you saw up there?"

"Oh," said Boots, "nothing more than a spade. That was what we heard."

The Magic Walnut

So they went on again a good bit until they came to a brook. They were thirsty, all three.

"I wonder now," said Boots, "where all this water comes from."

"Where the brook comes from, indeed!" said Peter and Paul. "Have you never heard how water rises from a spring in the earth?"

"Yes, but still I've a great fancy to see where this brook comes from," said Boots.

So along beside the brook he went, up and up. The brook got smaller and smaller. At last, what do you think he saw? Why, a great walnut, and out of that the water trickled.

"Good-day!" said Boots again. "So you lie here, and trickle and run down all alone?"

"Yes, I do," said the walnut. "Here have I trickled and run these hundreds of years, waiting for you, Boots."

"Well, here I am," said Boots. He took a lump of moss and plugged up the hole. Then, putting the walnut into his bag, he climbed down again.

"Well, now," said Peter and Paul, "have you found out where the water comes from? A rare sight it must have been!"

"Oh, after all, it was only a hole it ran out of," said Boots. The others laughed again. But Boots didn't mind.

"After all, I had the fun of seeing it," said he.

So when they had gone a bit farther, they came to the King's palace. But everyone in the kingdom had heard how he might win the Princess and half the realm, if he could only fell the big oak and dig the King's well. So many had come to try their luck that the oak was now *twice* as stout and big as it had been at first! The King had laid down a punishment. If anyone tried and could not fell the oak, he should be put on a desert island.

The brothers did not let themselves be scared by that, however. Peter, as the eldest, was to try his hand first. But it went with him as with all the rest who had hewn at the oak. For every chip he had cut out, two grew in its place. So the King's men seized him, bound him hand and foot, and put him out on the island.

Now, Paul was to try his luck. But he fared just the same. When he had hewn two or three strokes, they began to see the oak grow. So the King's men seized him too, bound him hand and foot, and put him out on the island. And now Boots was to try.

"You can save yourself the trouble. We'll bind you just as well first as last," laughed the King's men.

"Well, I'd just like to try first," said Boots. Taking his ax out of his bag, he fitted it to the haft.

"Hew away!" said he to his ax. Away it hewed, making the chips fly. It wasn't long before down came the oak.

When that was done, Boots pulled out his spade and fitted it to its handle.

"Dig away!" said he. The spade began to dig till the earth and rocks flew out in splinters. Boots soon had the well dug out.

And when he had got it as big and deep as he chose, Boots took out his walnut. He laid it in one corner of the well. He pulled the plug of moss out.

"Trickle and run," said Boots. So the water trickled and ran, till the well was brimful.

Then Boots had felled the oak which shaded the King's palace, and dug a well that held water all the year around. So he got the Princess and half the kingdom, as the King had said.

Gudbrand-on-the-Hillside

Retold by Gudrun Thorne-Thomsen

Once upon a time, there was a man whose name was Gudbrand. He had a farm which lay far, far away upon a hillside. So they called him Gudbrand-on-the-Hillside.

Now, this man and his good wife lived so happily together that everything the husband did the wife thought well done. She was always pleased at whatever he turned his hand to. The farm was their own land. They had a hundred dollars lying at the bottom of their chest and two cows in their farmyard.

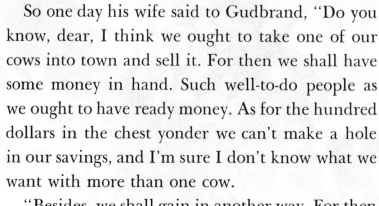

So one day his wife said to Gudbrand, "Do you know, dear, I think we ought to take one of our cows into town and sell it. For then we shall have some money in hand. Such well-to-do people as we ought to have ready money. As for the hundred dollars in the chest yonder we can't make a hole in our savings, and I'm sure I don't know what we want with more than one cow.

"Besides, we shall gain in another way. For then I shall get off with only looking after one cow instead of two."

Gudbrand thought his wife talked right good sense. So he set off at once with the cow to sell her. But when he got to town, no one would buy his cow.

"Well, well, never mind," said Gudbrand. "At the worst I can only go back home with my cow. The road is no farther out than in." And with that, he started home again with his cow.

But when he had gone a bit of the way, a man met him who had a horse to sell. Gudbrand thought it better to have a horse than a cow. So he traded with the man. A little farther on he met a man driving a fat pig before him. Gudbrand

thought it better to have a fat pig than a horse.
So he traded with the man.

After that he went a little farther, and a man
met him with a goat. Gudbrand thought it better
to have a goat than a pig. He traded with the man
who owned the goat. Then he went on a good bit
till he met a man who had a sheep. He traded with
him too, for Gudbrand thought it always better to
have a sheep than a goat.

After a while he met a man with a goose. He
traded away the sheep for the goose. And when
he had walked a long, long time he met a man with
a cock, and he traded with *him*. For he thought,
"It is surely better to have a cock than a goose."

Then he went on till the day was far spent. He
began to get very hungry. So he sold the cock and
bought food with the money. For, thought Gudbrand-on-the-Hillside, "It is always better to save
one's life than to have a cock."

After that, he went on homeward till he reached
his nearest neighbor's house. There he turned in.

"Well," said the owner of the house, "how did
things go with you in town?"

"Rather so-so," said Gudbrand. "I can't praise

my luck, nor do I blame it either." And with that he told the whole story from first to last.

"Ah!" said his friend. "You'll get nicely hauled over the coals when you go home to your wife. I wouldn't stand in your shoes."

"Well," said Gudbrand-on-the-Hillside, "I have so kind a wife she never has a word to say against anything that I do."

"Oh!" answered his neighbor. "I hear what you say, but I don't believe it for all that."

"And so you doubt it?" asked Gudbrand-on-the-Hillside.

"Yes," said the friend. "I have a hundred crowns at the bottom of my chest. I will give them to you if you can prove what you say."

So Gudbrand stayed till it began to get dark. Then they went together to his house. The neighbor was to stand outside the door and listen, while the man went in to his wife.

Will She Be Kind?

"Good evening!" said Gudbrand.

"Good evening!" said the good wife. "Oh! is that you? Now I am happy." Then she asked how things had gone with him in town.

"Oh, only so-so," answered Gudbrand. "Not much to brag of. When I got to town, there was no one who would buy the cow. So I traded it away for a horse."

"For a horse!" said his wife. "Well, that is good

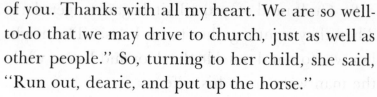

of you. Thanks with all my heart. We are so well-to-do that we may drive to church, just as well as other people." So, turning to her child, she said, "Run out, dearie, and put up the horse."

"Ah!" said Gudbrand. "But you see I have not the horse after all. When I got a bit farther on the road, I traded it for a pig."

"Think of that, now!" said the wife. "You did just as I should have done myself. A thousand thanks! Now I can have a bit of bacon in the house to set before people when they come to see me, that I can. What do we want with a horse? People would only say we had got so proud that we couldn't walk to church. Go out, child, and put the pig in the sty."

"But I have not the pig either," said Gudbrand. "A little farther on, I traded it for a goat."

"Dear me!" cried the wife. "How well you manage everything! Now I think it over, what should I do with a pig? Now I shall have milk and cheese. Run out, child, and put up the goat."

"Nay, but I haven't the goat either," said Gudbrand. "A little farther on I traded it away and got a fine sheep instead!"

"You don't say so!" cried the wife. "Why, you do everything to please me, just as if I had been with you. What do we want with a goat? Now if I have a sheep, I shall have both wool and clothing. Run out, child, and put up the sheep."

"But I haven't the sheep any more than the rest," said Gudbrand. "I traded it away for a goose."

"Thank you, thank you, with all my heart," cried his wife. "What should I do with a sheep? I have no spinning wheel or carding comb. We can buy clothes as we have always done. Now I shall have roast goose, which I have longed for so often. Run out, child, and put up the goose!"

"Well!" said Gudbrand, "I haven't the goose either. I traded it for a cock."

"Dear me!" cried his wife. "How you think of everything! A cock! Why, it's as good as an eight-day clock. Every day the cock crows at four o'clock, and we shall be able to stir our stiff legs in good time. Run out, child, and put up the cock."

"But after all, I haven't the cock either," said Gudbrand. "For I was forced to sell the cock, for fear I should starve."

"Now, God be praised that you did so!" cried his wife. "Whatever you do, you do it always just after my own heart. What should we do with the cock? We are our own masters, I should think, and can lie abed in the morning as long as we like. Heaven be thanked that I have you safe back again. You do everything so well that I want neither cock nor goose, neither pig nor cow."

Then Gudbrand opened the door and said, "Well, what do you say now? Have I won the hundred crowns?"

And his neighbor was forced to admit that he had.

Mr. Murdle's Large Heart

Margery Bianco

In nearly every town you will find one store which keeps all those foolish little things that the other stores forget. Mr. Murdle's is just such a store. Many, many years ago, when Mr. Murdle was a round-faced little boy, he must have said to his mother, "When I grow up, I'm going to keep a store!"

He had no idea at all what he wanted to sell in his store. It was just going to be a store. He started by buying a little bit here and a little bit there. All sorts of funny cardboard boxes began to pile up on his shelves.

He thought of ginger ale and slate pencils and newspapers, and of course candy. He remembered little plastic dolls and hairpins and pencil sharpeners, and ash trays with scalloped gilt edges. Mr. Murdle himself doesn't really know all that he has in his store.

But if ever you want to buy something that you cannot find in any of the other stores, sooner or later someone will say, "Well, you *might* try Mr. Murdle, across the way!"

Sure enough, after Mr. Murdle has stood for a moment thinking, he will rummage about among his cardboard boxes and pull one of them out. And nine times out of ten, there is the very thing you were looking for!

All this is wonderful enough. But it isn't the most remarkable thing about Mr. Murdle.

The most remarkable thing about Mr. Murdle is his Large Heart.

Everyone who knows Mr. Murdle will tell you what a Large Heart he has. And it is really true. I have seen it myself, hanging up at the back of Mr. Murdle's store. It is pink and purple, with yellow around the edges. In the middle, which is white, there are rows of little elastic loops, which once upon a time held tiny bottles of pink and purple and yellow lozenges.

It is a fine thing for anyone to have such a Large Heart. But there are disadvantages also, especially for anyone like Mr. Murdle, who ought to be thinking of money every minute, as the other storekeepers do. That Large Heart of his is always getting in the way.

Suppose a little girl wants an ice-cream cone

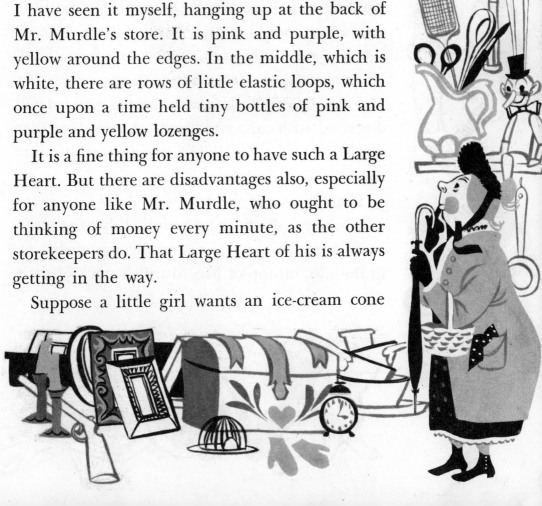

and has only three cents. Or suppose some little boy wants candy, and Mr. Murdle knows perfectly well he should only give five chocolates for a nickel. Then that Large Heart begins to whisper to Mr. Murdle. Before he knows it, he has handed out the cone with an extra lump of strawberry ice cream on. Or he has slipped seven chocolates into the bag instead of five.

Then there are the cats.

It began with one cat. She found that the pleasantest place to spend the morning was curled up in the sun, on top of Mr. Murdle's stack of daily papers. Mr. Murdle used to give her the melted ice cream that was left over at night.

Presently she married and had a family. They all came to live in Mr. Murdle's store. Now there were eleven cats, and not nearly enough melted ice cream to go around. So Mr. Murdle—having such a Large Heart—took to melting the ice cream on purpose. He found that the cats liked vanilla best. So he always ordered more of the vanilla than of any other kind.

Everyone liked Mr. Murdle, including the cats. Mr. Murdle himself was one of the happiest people in the world, and all on account of his Large Heart.

But there was one person who did not approve of Mr. Murdle's Large Heart. This was Mr. Murdle's aunt. It may seem funny for Mr. Murdle, who is at least forty and quite bald on the top of his head, to have an aunt. But he had, and one fine day she came to keep house for him.

She was a busy, active sort of woman. She was not content with just managing Mr. Murdle's house. She soon began to manage his store as well.

She didn't approve of the cats. She didn't

approve of the little boys and girls. In fact, she
didn't approve of anything at all that Mr. Murdle
liked, and least of all of the way he did business.
She decided that sort of thing must be changed.

Mr. Murdle Loses His Heart

At first she didn't have much success. Mr.
Murdle had been going along in his own way for
so long that it wasn't easy, even for a determined
person like Mr. Murdle's aunt, to change him.
But she did her best. And as luck would have it,
while she was tidying the store one day, she came
upon Mr. Murdle's Large Heart.

She didn't at all know what it was, but she certainly didn't like the look of it. She leaned on her broom and stared.

"Now that's a foolish sort of thing," she said. "Cluttering the store up and taking space where it isn't wanted. I'm just going to throw it out!"

And she did.

From that moment, a very dreadful change came over Mr. Murdle.

The aunt thought it was all due to her good advice. But it wasn't at all. It was just because Mr. Murdle had lost his Large Heart.

In two days, you wouldn't have known Mr. Murdle's store.

Everything was tidy. Mr. Murdle himself was just as businesslike as he could be. He knew the price of everything. When little boys asked for a nickel's worth of candy, believe me, they *got* a nickel's worth of candy, and not one bit more. If the little girls hadn't enough money for their ice-cream cones, they could just turn right around and walk out again.

It was terrible. As for the cats, they all left in a body and went to live with the fat lady at the delicatessen. Mr. Murdle said he couldn't afford to feed a lot of lazy cats that did nothing but sleep all day. Moreover, they mussed up his newspapers.

Can you *imagine* that!

All the little boys and girls were very upset. But, luckily, there was one little boy with more sense than the rest.

He was looking around in the store one day. Mr. Murdle's aunt happened to be away shopping, or she would have chased him out. But there he was, staring about, and trying to make out why everything looked so different. All at once, he realized that something was missing.

It was Mr. Murdle's Large Heart.

It wasn't in its usual place above the counter. It wasn't anywhere in the store. Being a clever little boy, he soon put two and two together.

"I bet you," he said, "that mean old woman has thrown it out!"

He went straight into the yard behind the store and began to hunt. Sure enough, there he found it, thrown out with a pile of broken boxes waiting to be burned.

It was torn at one side and a bit crumpled. But he smoothed it out and carried it back to its old place on the wall behind the counter. To make sure this time, he got a hammer and nails and he *nailed* it, all around the edge.

Not even Mr. Murdle's aunt could have torn it down again!

What's more, she never got a chance. For as soon as Mr. Murdle set foot in the store, now that his Large Heart was back, he became just the same Mr. Murdle that he had been before.

The very first thing he did was to send his aunt packing. Then he telephoned for fresh ice cream —every kind he could think of. He opened all the candy boxes and told the little boys and girls, who by this time had heard the news, that they might help themselves.

And he dragged his old armchair out and settled down, as happy as could be. When the cats saw that, they all came trooping back again too.

So today things are just as they used to be. There is very little danger they will ever change again. Not so long as Mr. Murdle's Large Heart stays there, right in its place.

And if you don't believe me, all you need to do is walk into Mr. Murdle's store and ask for a nickel's worth of candy. You will see how much you get!

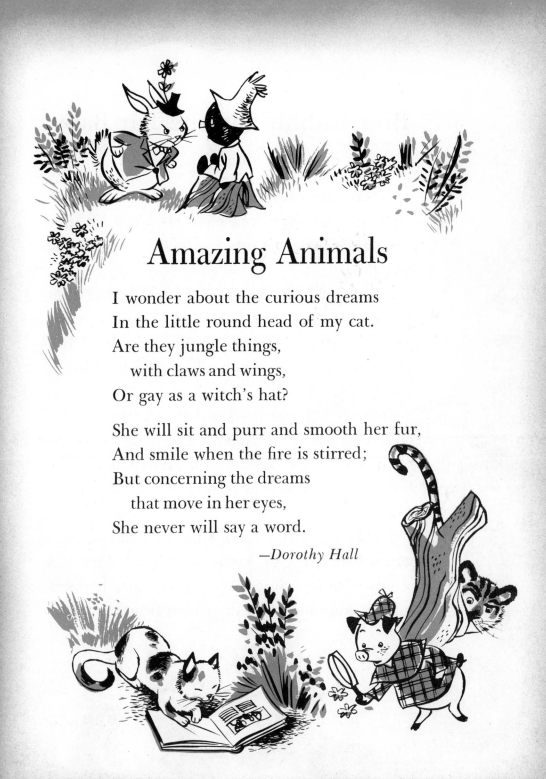

Amazing Animals

I wonder about the curious dreams
In the little round head of my cat.
Are they jungle things,
   with claws and wings,
Or gay as a witch's hat?

She will sit and purr and smooth her fur,
And smile when the fire is stirred;
But concerning the dreams
   that move in her eyes,
She never will say a word.

—*Dorothy Hall*

Brer Rabbit and the Tar Baby

Retold by Anne Malcolmson

Now old Brer Rabbit was as sly and mischievous a fellow as has ever been seen. He spent his time playing tricks on the other animals, especially on Brer Fox.

Time after time, Brer Fox thought he had Brer Rabbit under his thumb. He licked his chops and filled his kettle, expecting to dine off rabbit. But time after time the cottontail made a fool out of the greedy fox.

Now the fox was tired of being tricked by his long-eared friend. His mouth watered for a steaming plate of stew—rabbit stew. What's more, he thought he knew how he could solve both problems at once.

Brer Fox fancied himself an artist. Some careless person had left a bucket of tar about. This was exactly what he wanted. With great pains he went to work and modeled a little man from the sticky

black stuff. It was a fine statue, life-sized. On its head, Master Fox placed an old straw hat. It certainly looked real.

So old Brer Fox placed the little tar fellow beside the road. Then he hid himself in the bushes to see the fun.

Soon, clippety-clop, down the road came Brer Rabbit. Being a friendly soul, Master Rabbit stopped to say "Howdy!" to the little black stranger. The tar baby, of course, said nothing.

"Good morning," said the rabbit, a little louder. He tipped his hat. The tar baby said nothing at all.

This seemed rude to Brer Rabbit. All the animals, even the fox and the wolf, said "Howdy" to one another.

Brer Rabbit walked up closer. He yelled, "Nice weather we're having," at the black figure. Still the tar baby said nothing.

"Well," snorted the rabbit, "you're stuck-up,

aren't you? Don't you know enough to speak when you're spoken to? If you don't, I'll slap your sassy face."

The tar baby, of course, said nothing. The rabbit was as good as his word. He slapped the tar baby with his right paw. This was what the fox had planned all along. The paw stuck fast in the sticky tar.

Brer Rabbit was becoming angry. "Let me go!" he raged. "You're not only stuck-up. You're mean. If you don't let me go, I'll slap you with my other hand."

When the tar baby paid no attention, Brer Rabbit reached out and slapped him again with his left paw. It stuck, too. The fox, hiding in the underbrush, had to hold his sides to keep from laughing out loud.

Then the rabbit began to kick. First he kicked with his right foot. It stuck fast in the tar. Then he kicked with his left. He was furious.

"If you don't let me go," he yelled, "I'll butt you with my head, you low-down, mean, stuck-up thing, you!" The tar baby sat as still as a lump on a log. Brer Rabbit butted.

Here he was, completely stuck up in the ball of tar! He couldn't budge.

The fox came out from his hiding place with tears of laughter falling down his cheeks. His little joke had worked perfectly. He and Mrs. Fox and all the little foxes would have themselves a feast.

Immediately Brer Rabbit saw that he had fallen into a trap. For all his slyness, he had been caught. But he didn't turn a hair when he saw Mr. Fox. His mind began to work faster than it had ever worked before.

Turning to the fox, he put on his saddest

expression. Crocodile tears came to his eyes. "You've finally caught me, Mr. Fox," he sniffed. "Yes, I know I've been mean to you in my day and I deserve anything and everything you will do to me . . . *(sniff!)* . . . I'm sorry for all the trouble I've caused you. Really, I am, dear Mr. Fox . . . *(sniff!)* . . . I've been a selfish, mischievous, horrid rabbit. . . . Do with me what you like."

Brer Fox was pleased with himself. He let the rabbit go on with his humble apologies.

"Do anything you wish, dear Mr. Fox," sobbed Brer Rabbit, looking up quickly to see how his enemy was taking his talk, "anything at all. . . . But please, kind Mr. Fox, don't throw me in the briar patch. Roast me alive! I deserve that."

The fox scratched his head. "It's too much trouble to build a fire," he said. "I think I'll hang you instead."

"Oh, hang me, please, hang me," begged the rabbit, looking very humble. "Hang me from the highest tree in the forest. But don't throw me in the briar patch."

"I haven't any string," said the fox. "I'll have to drown you."

"Drown me, then," said the rabbit, pretending to be faint with fear. "I don't care any more. Drown me, if you wish, but please, oh, please, *don't* throw me in the *briar patch.*"

This time Brer Fox lost his head. He said to himself, "If he's so afraid of the briar patch, that's the very thing. I'll throw him in right away."

Without any more talk, the fox picked up the rabbit by the leg. He swung him around his head and threw him as hard as he could into the middle of the briar bushes. This, of course, was exactly what Brer Rabbit wanted him to do. The thorns scratched the tar from his hands and feet and head. In a flash, he had scrambled free and was off up the hill.

The next thing Brer Fox knew, his rabbit stew was sitting at the top of the hill as saucily as ever. He had been fooled again!

"I was born and bred in a briar patch," sang the rabbit as he disappeared over the hilltop. "Born and bred in a briar patch."

Kattor

Georgia Travers

Kattor was a young tiger. He had a beautiful coat of yellow, striped with black. His paws were as big as the boughs of a young tree and his tail was long and swishy. His eyes were yellow and fierce, even for a small tiger's.

Kattor lived with his mother in a den of rocks in a hillside. Here he had a bed of dry crackly leaves.

As he grew a little older his mother began taking Kattor out for exercise. Then he would jump about, turn somersaults, toss sticks into the air and tear leaves to pieces with his sharp, sharp claws. He would pounce in fun at stones and shadows.

Many months went by. Then one day Kattor ventured out all alone. He sharpened his claws on a great tall tree. He struck playfully at objects in his path. It was fun to crush them at a single blow. And then he noticed something else! Wherever he went, all the other little creatures of the woods ran away screaming for their lives. This was very thrilling. How big and powerful he was!

That evening he went home and told his mother all he had done.

"I am a great strong tiger, am I not?" said Kattor.

"You are a strong baby tiger," said his mother. "But now you must sleep," and she fluffed up his bed of leaves, washed him tenderly with her great rough tongue and purred to him softly as he went to sleep.

Every day after that Kattor went a little farther from home. Every day he sharpened his claws— and every day he dared to frighten bigger and bigger animals and to strike at bigger and bigger things to make them fall. And every night he would return to his mother and say as before: "Mother, I am a great strong tiger, am I not?" And every night his mother would reply, "You are a strong baby tiger." Then she would wash him tenderly with her great rough tongue, fluff up his bed of leaves and purr softly to him until he went to sleep.

This went on for a long, long time. Then one day he went to hunt for food for the first time and brought it home proudly to show his mother.

"Mother, I am a great strong tiger, am I not?" said Kattor. And that night his mother answered, "Yes, Kattor, you are getting to be a great strong tiger."

"Some day I will conquer the world for you," said Kattor.

"Do well what tigers can do, Kattor," said his mother softly. "It is all I ask." And she washed him tenderly with her great rough tongue, fluffed up his bed of leaves and purred softly to him until he went to sleep.

The Storm

One morning as Kattor was about to go out for his daily exercise he noticed that it was darker than usual. "What is it, Mother?" asked Kattor.

"It is a storm," said his mother.

And just then the storm broke in all its fury. The rain came in torrents, the heavens growled like thousands of angry tigers, and trees crashed before the door of the den.

"Who is strong enough to break down great trees?" asked Kattor.

"It is the wind," said his mother.

"I will conquer the wind," said Kattor, and he rushed out into the storm.

"Go away, Wind, or I will scratch you," called Kattor. The wind only roared louder than before.

"Go away, Wind," cried Kattor, but his voice was drowned by the fury of the storm.

Kattor struck again and again into the air. The wind only grew stronger and drove the rain into his eyes. Still Kattor fought, saying, "I will conquer you. I will, I will." And still the wind roared and drove rain against Kattor's body until finally he was so tired that he almost believed he could fight no longer.

Then, as suddenly as it had come, the storm stopped. Kattor stood still for a moment, astonished, and then ran joyfully in to see his mother.

"See, Mother, I have conquered the wind!"

His mother again said, "Kattor, do well the things tigers can do. Then you will always be happy." And she smoothed his fur with her great rough tongue and he slept.

When he woke up he felt more powerful than
ever. He set out for further conquests.

This time he walked until he came to a great
mountain.

"Get out of my way, Mountain," said Kattor.

He scratched and tore at the mountain side. His
sharp claws caught in the crevices of the rocks and

his paws stung with pain. The sand got into Kattor's eyes and hurt him unbearably.

And now the sun was beginning to set. It shone directly over the top of the mountain; it beat into Kattor's smarting, sand-filled eyes. Kattor could not go on, but he was determined not to be beaten.

"Oh, Mountain-under-the-sun, I will conquer you in the morning," he said.

So he went home to his mother. She fed him, fluffed his bed of leaves and with her great rough tongue she smoothed his fur and purred softly until he went to sleep.

"I *am* a great strong tiger," said Kattor as he was falling to sleep, "am I not?"

"You are a strong young tiger," said his mother and he slept.

The next morning he rose early to conquer the mountain. He had forgotten just where the mountain was, but he remembered that it was under the sun. Baby tiger that he was, he did not know that the evening sun which he had seen over the mountain was in the west, and that the morning sun which was just rising was in the east. So he went east instead of west.

He walked and walked. And still he found no mountain. And then suddenly a quiver of delight ran through his yellow body from the tip of his ears to the end of his long swishy tail. He had scared away the mountain after all. How strong and powerful he was!

He walked and walked and soon he came to more water than he had ever seen in his life before. It was the sea.

"Get out of my way, Water," said Kattor to it fiercely, "or I will scratch you!" but the water only

kept on lapping peacefully against the shore.

This made Kattor very angry. He rushed at the sea. He bit and tore and clawed at it but he could not grasp it. No matter how hard he struck at the water, it only closed peacefully over his paws as though it could not be hurt.

Kattor Conquers the Sea

Kattor, who liked to be dry and warm and comfortable, became more and more angry. He fought and fought. Water got into his nose and eyes, and he was very uncomfortable. Finally, after a long, long time he felt that he could not go on. Turning his back toward the sea, he started unsteadily for home. But what was this which greeted his eyes as he turned? Vast stretches of wet sand lay before him. He, being a baby tiger, did not know that during his long struggle with the water the tide had gone out. He believed that he had chased the water far out into the sea!

"I am, after all, the most powerful tiger in the whole world," thought Kattor, and with renewed strength he ran home to tell his mother.

"Mother," he said, breathlessly, "I conquered the wind, I frightened the mountain, and now I have scared the water away. I am a great strong tiger."

"You are still young, but you are a great strong tiger," said his mother as she washed him with her great rough tongue, and fluffed up his bed of leaves. Then she added softly as she purred him to sleep, "Tomorrow I will go with you."

And so the next day his mother went with him.

"I have something I want you to see," said his mother.

She led him up a high cliff where he had never been before. It was hard climbing, and they came to the ridge of a hill. Scarcely had Kattor put his head over the top of the hill when he felt a strong, strong breeze blowing over its edge.

"It is the wind," said Kattor's mother simply, and Kattor wondered how the wind had dared to

come back. But before he was able to say anything, he saw in the distance the great mountain he thought he had frightened away.

"It is the mountain," said Kattor's mother.

Puzzled thoughts gathered in poor Kattor's mind. Hadn't he chased the mountain and the wind away? But when he wanted to ask his mother, he found that she had wandered to the far edge of the hill and seemed to be looking away off into the distance. Kattor went to his mother, and there before him lay the water he thought he had conquered.

"It is the sea," said his mother.

That evening his mother fluffed up his bed and smoothed his soft fur with her great rough tongue.

"Am I *not* a great strong tiger?" asked Kattor.

"Yes, Kattor, you are a great strong tiger," said his mother gently, "but it takes more than a great strong tiger to move the winds or the mountains or the sea." And she purred softly until Kattor fell asleep.

And then, as though in a dream, he seemed to hear her add softly, "Do what tigers can do, Kattor. Then you will always be happy."

The Mystery of Egbert

Walter R. Brooks

Freddy was really a very clever pig. So when he found a book about the great detective Sherlock Holmes, he decided to be a detective, too. One of his early cases was brought to him by Mrs. Winnick, a poor rabbit widow with a large family.

"Oh, Mr. Freddy," Mrs. Winnick burst out, "it's about Egbert. He's disappeared, and whatever I shall do I don't know. He was always such a good boy, too—kind and helpful, and willing to look after the baby. With the other children it's play, play, play all day long, but Egbert—" And she began to cry.

Freddy was not greatly disturbed by her tears. White rabbits are very sentimental and tender-hearted little animals. They cry a good deal.

"Come, come," said Freddy briskly. "Just tell me all about it, and we'll see what can be done. Let's see—Egbert. He's your eighth oldest, isn't he? Or ninth?"

"Twelfth," she replied, "and always such a good—"

"Yes," said Freddy quickly. "And when did you last see him?"

After asking a good many questions, Freddy got Mrs. Winnick's story. The night before, Egbert had taken several of the children up through the woods to Jones's Creek to get some watercress. At nine o'clock, the children had come home without him. They had not found any good watercress, and Egbert had said that he would go farther down the creek. Mrs. Winnick had put the children to bed and had gone to bed herself. But this morning Egbert's bed was empty. He had not come home.

"I'll get to work on it right away," Freddy said. "Don't worry. I'll soon have Egbert back for you."

Mrs. Winnick went off home, stopping after every three or four hops to cry a little and blow her nose. Freddy set out at once for the creek. He found the watercress bed which Egbert had visited with his little brothers and sisters. Then Freddy went slowly on downstream, keeping a sharp lookout. Once he saw where some wintergreen leaves had been nibbled. Once, in a sandy place, he saw the plain print of a rabbit's foot. And then, where the stream widened out, he found another big bed of cress. In the swampy shore were a large number of rabbits' footprints.

Freddy had been very happy when he started out. Here was a new problem. He would solve it and prove to his friends that he was a real detective after all. But now this problem was just as bad as the other one. These were Egbert's footprints all right. But what good did they do him? There ought to be some clue that he could follow up.

"You can't solve a case without clues," he said to himself unhappily. "These might be clues to Sherlock Holmes, but to me they're just a lot of footprints." And he sat down on the bank to think.

He was thinking so hard that for some time he did not see a small rabbit who hopped out of the woods and made several trips to the cress bed before Freddy caught sight of him.

The rabbit hadn't seen Freddy, either. When the pig started up suddenly, he hid behind a bush.

"So *you're* the one who made all those footprints in the mud here, are you?" said Freddy.

"Yes, sir," came a small, anxious voice from behind the bush. "Isn't it all right, sir?"

"Sure it's all right," said the pig. "Come out. I won't hurt you. I'm looking for a rabbit about your size. Haven't seen one around, have you?"

The rabbit hopped timidly out. "No, sir," he said. "Who was he, sir?"

"Ah," said Freddy mysteriously, *"I'm* the one to be asking the questions. I'm a detective. Just you answer up briskly, young fellow. Haven't seen any other rabbits around, eh?"

"No, sir—"

"No other footprints when you came?"

"I don't think so, sir. You see, I—"

"How long have you been here?" asked Freddie.

"Since last night, sir. You see, I came to get some watercress, and as I was—"

Freddy stopped him. "That's enough," he said severely. "Please just answer the questions I ask you, yes or no. You heard no unusual noises?"

"Yes, sir—I mean no, sir," said the rabbit, who was getting mixed up.

"What do you mean—'yes, sir, no, sir?'" said Freddy. "Please give me a straight answer. Did you or did you not hear any unusual noises?"

"No, sir—I mean—" the rabbit swallowed, "—no, sir."

The Witness Breaks Down

"Good," said the pig. "And—ha, h'm, let me see—" He couldn't think of any more questions to ask. "Well, ah, what are you doing here anyway?"

But the rabbit didn't answer. "Come, come,"

said Freddy sharply. "Answer me! What are you—"

The rabbit burst into tears. "You told me to answer yes or no," he sobbed. "You can't answer that question yes or no. I c-came here to get water-cress, and I was just going home and I found a little bird with a hurt wing, and I thought I ought to stay with it, and I know my mother'll worry. B-but I don't like to leave the bird all alone, and now you come and ask me a lot of questions, and . . ." He cried so hard that he got the hiccups.

"There, there," said Freddy, patting the rabbit on the back. "I'm sorry I scared you. It's all right. Where is this bird?"

"Up in a hollow behind that tree," hiccuped the little animal.

"All right," said Freddy. "I'll look after him for you. I've got to find this other rabbit I was telling you about. You run along home."

The rabbit trotted off, still crying, and hiccuping now and then through his tears. Freddy went in search of the bird. He found it presently—a wood thrush too young to talk yet. Beside this bird was a small heap of watercress which the rabbit had been trying to feed it.

"Tut, tut," said Freddy. "Feeding an infant like that watercress! He'll be sick. That rabbit has a kind heart, but he certainly isn't very bright." He picked up the little thrush carefully and carried it out into an open space. Then he went back into the bushes and sat down. In five minutes there was a rush of wings, and the mother thrush lit beside the hungry baby bird. Freddy slipped away without waiting to be thanked.

"Now," he said to himself, "for Egbert. I wish I'd never tried to be a detective, that's what I wish."

Freddy searched and searched—along the creek and in the woods. He sat down to rest under a beech-tree—and realized suddenly that he didn't know where he was. "Well, I suppose the best thing to do is to keep on going," he said to himself. "May come across a squirrel or a jay who can tell me where I am."

But though he walked and walked, he met no one. He had just about decided that he would have to stay out all night when he noticed some foot-prints. "H'm, someone has been along here not many minutes ago," he said. "Looks like a pig, too. I guess I'll follow and see if I can catch up."

So he went on, following the footprints, until he came to a place where the other pig had sat down to rest. There was the plain print of a curly tail in the loose earth under a beech-tree. Freddy sat down too. Then suddenly something about the place seemed familiar to him.

"Why, this is where I sat down to rest myself a long time ago! Those are my own footprints I've been following!"

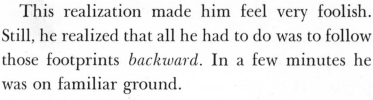

This realization made him feel very foolish. Still, he realized that all he had to do was to follow those footprints *backward*. In a few minutes he was on familiar ground.

"I'll just stop in and see if anything has been heard of Egbert," he said to himself. So he turned down toward the Widow Winnick's home.

Half a dozen small rabbits were playing about on the edge of the woods as he came up. One of them called down the rabbit hole, "Mother! Mr. Freddy's here!"

Almost at once, Mrs. Winnick's head popped up. But it was a changed Mrs. Winnick that beamed happily at him.

"Oh, Mr. Freddy!" she cried. "How can I ever thank you? My Egbert! You found him for me!"

"But," stammered the bewildered Freddy, "I didn't—" And then he stopped. For one of the little rabbits hiccuped and said politely, "Excuse me." And Freddy saw it all. That rabbit had been Egbert all the time!

"Oh, don't thank me, Mrs. Winnick. Don't thank me," Freddy said, rather grandly. "It was nothing, I assure you—nothing at all."

Serapina Takes Charge

Anne H. White

The moment Mrs. Salinus laid eyes on the cat Serapina, she felt that Serapina was different. Serapina had one brown eye and one blue eye. She could appear and disappear. She could make her tail longer or shorter, and open doors with it. Mr. Salinus and the children were delighted with Serapina, but Mrs. Salinus had her doubts.

The morning after Serapina came to live with them, Mr. Salinus was not waked up by his alarm clock. A soft, gargling sound in his left ear woke him. It was Serapina, sitting on his pillow.

Mr. Salinus tried to push her aside. But Serapina simply moved over toward his right ear and gargled louder. Mr. Salinus sat up and glared at her. Then he looked at his clock. It was exactly six-forty-five, and the alarm was turned off.

"That's strange," Mr. Salinus said. He got out of bed and into his bathrobe and slippers. "I'm sure I set the alarm last night."

"It's a good thing the cat happened to wake you," Mrs. Salinus murmured sleepily.

"Come to think of it, I don't think she did *happen* to," Mr. Salinus said. "I'll bet she plans what she does. Don't you, old girl?" he asked. But Serapina wasn't there.

When he was dressed, Mr. Salinus started his routine. But when he went into Sally's room he was too late. Serapina had just finished pulling the covers off Sally very neatly. With her front paws, she pulled them back on one side. Then, jumping across Sally, she pulled them back on the other side. Every time Serapina jumped, Sally bounced gently on the mattress. It was like being rocked awake instead of rocked asleep.

When she had waked Sally, Serapina jumped

off the bed and hustled into Peter's room. Peter was lying on his back reading a comic book. Serapina stopped that. She sat on his stomach and thwacked the book with her tail. When he turned over on his stomach, Serapina sat on his back and tickled him with her front paws. Peter got up.

Serapina went into Bobby's room. This particular morning, Bobby was hiding in the bottom of his bed. Serapina went down to the bottom and shoveled him up to the top with her broad, hard head.

As soon as she had got the children up, she hurried to the kitchen to join Mr. and Mrs. Salinus. She opened the back door with no trouble at all. Wrapping the end of her tail firmly around the neck of a milk bottle, she dragged it into the kitchen. She stood each bottle on the floor beside the refrigerator.

When she had brought in all the milk, she got the oranges by jumping into the vegetable bin and turning around a few times. The oranges flew out in all directions. Serapina rolled them over to Mr. Salinus with her front paws. Then she hustled back upstairs to see about the children.

Serapina Takes Over

Of course, Sally and Peter had dressed themselves for years. They just needed a little prodding and reminding. Serapina was excellent at both. When she thought a child had dawdled

enough, she stretched out her tail the required
number of notches and prodded firmly.

She proved just as good at reminding, too.
Anxiously, she watched Sally pass the dresser
many times, always forgetting to brush her hair.
So she waited until Sally bent down to tie her
shoes. Her hair fell forward as she leaned. Serapina quickly reached out her paw. Gently she
clawed a lock of hair and stuck on a snarl.

"Why, Serapina!" Sally exclaimed, untangling
hair and claw. "I will brush my hair right away."

Serapina waited till Sally picked up the brush.
Then she went into Peter's room. Peter also was
tying his shoes. But instead of bending down to
reach the laces, Peter bent up. He was lying on
his back with one leg waving over his head.
Serapina could not have asked for a better chance
to remind him to wash his face. She sat close beside
him and wiped his face with her toes. It was a
rough sort of washrag, but Peter got the idea.

Presently Mrs. Salinus called everyone to
breakfast, asking that somebody please find
Bobby.

"I bet I know who will!" Sally sang out. And she was right. As the family sat down, Bobby appeared. Serapina had found him in the coat closet and was conducting him to the dining room. Perhaps "bumping" him would be a better word for it. Bobby was just the right size for a large cat to bump. Serapina succeeded in blocking every move he made *away* from the dining room by giving him a bump *toward* it.

Mrs. Salinus began dishing up the cereal. "One of you help Bobby pull up his chair," she reminded the older children.

"We don't have to, Mummy," Peter and Sally said together. "Serapina—"

"No!" Mrs. Salinus almost screamed. "No, no! I won't believe it!" But she had to, poor woman. There was Bobby pushing his chair. There was Serapina pulling it, her tail crooked over the lower rung.

Mrs. Salinus clasped her head in her hands. "That finishes it!" she cried. "James, there is something very strange about a cat that does all the things that cat does. And that tail! And those eyes! James, that is a very queer cat. In fact, for a cat, it is unheard of. Well," Mrs. Salinus rushed on, "I won't have something unheard of in my house. It makes me nervous. Besides, she is probably rare and valuable too. So you telephone The Unwanted Animal Society right away."

Mr. Salinus sighed. He did not mind having something unheard of in his house. He was an obliging man, however. He went to the telephone and asked for The Unwanted Animal Society. Sally and Peter stood close beside his elbow.

"Yes, yes," they heard a voice say. "We take cats if the owners do not want them."

"But," Mr. Salinus explained honestly, "I am not the owner."

"Then why," asked the voice, "do you own the cat?"

"I don't," Mr. Salinus answered. "I just have the cat."

"But you don't want it?"

"Yes, I do want it." Mr. Salinus spoke truthfully, but he did not look at his wife.

"Then why call us?" asked The Unwanted Animal Society and hung up.

Mr. Salinus, to please Mrs. Salinus, then called the police and reported he had a stray cat in his house. He talked to Officer Michael McCarthy. Mike McCarthy was a young policeman. His ambition was to catch a thief. He was not interested in animals, but he did look at the records in the Lost and Found Department. There was no word of a lost cat, so Mike could not be very helpful about a found one. He put Serapina's name down in the files, and Mr. Salinus hung up with a sigh of relief.

"We will keep Serapina with a clear conscience until we get an answer to the advertisement I put in the paper last night," he declared. He looked at his watch. "I must go!" he cried in a horrified voice, grabbing up his hat. "Take care of Serapina, my dears. She may be unheard of, or even valuable, but it strikes me she may be mighty useful too."

As the morning wore on, Mrs. Salinus realized

how very right Mr. Salinus could be. As she was sitting over her second cup of coffee and thinking some thoughts about cats, a slight rattling noise drew her attention. It was Serapina, the forgotten vitamin bottle held firmly in her tail, going in search of the children. In the excitement of the telephone calls everyone, except Serapina, had forgotten the vitamins.

Mrs. Salinus finished her coffee and gave up her thoughts. As she very sensibly put it, she really did not know what thoughts to think anyway.

Pino and Paint

Dan Noonan

If you had seen Pino riding along behind his father that day, you would have thought he was just like any other Indian boy in that part of the Southwest. And you would have been right—almost.

Like all the other boys, Pino lived in a house of sun-dried brick, called adobe. Like them, he spent much of his time helping his father and mother. Pino's parents made pottery painted with bright designs, which he was learning to copy. He played and ate and slept and grew, just like all the other boys.

Pino was like them in every way but one. He could not talk.

"Do not be concerned," Pino's father said often to his mother. "Some day our son will talk. And meanwhile, see how fast he learns."

It was true. There was not a boy around the
settlement whose eyes were brighter, whose ears
were keener, whose feet could run more swiftly,
or whose hands were more clever and sure.

There were many things Pino liked to do. Best
of all, he liked to go to the Indian agency with
his father when he went to sell the pottery and
buy supplies.

Pino liked everything about those days. He
liked the trip over the narrow trail to the settlement. Better still, he liked climbing up behind

his father and jogging along with the good solid feeling of a horse between his legs. How Pino wished that he might some day have a horse of his own!

All of the men sitting in the scant shade in front of the agency building called, "Hello there, Ata," to Pino's father and "Hello, Pino!" to Pino himself. Pino's father called back, "Hello, there!" Pino smiled and waved his hand.

Unloading the pottery, they carried it inside. While Ata bargained, Pino walked slowly around the dim room, eyeing the calico, moccasins, bright-labeled tins, the knives and tools, and sacks and boxes of goods. But in all the store nothing brought a gleam to Pino's eyes today. There was nothing he wanted but a horse.

Just as he was thinking of going out to sit on the step with the men, his father put a firm hand on his shoulder.

"This has been a good day," his father said. "We have sold all but that cracked pitcher."

Pino smiled his pleasure. He took the cracked pitcher from his father's hands. The two of them walked out together.

Now there was time to visit with the men. They used few words, but there was friendliness in their voices. A good trading day, they agreed. Good weather. Everything felt fine.

As they waited quietly between speeches, up came Tall Hat, the horse trader.

"How went everything with you, Tall Hat?" Pino's father asked. Pino stood by, listening.

"Pretty good, thanks," Tall Hat replied, "except for that pinto pony. That horse is loco. He lets no one ride him. I guess he is good for nothing. Every time, I am left with him on my hands." He sighed as he looked toward the pony. "I'd trade him for that cracked water pitcher."

All the men smiled at Tall Hat's joke. But

Pino did not know that it was a joke. He wanted that pony very much. So he silently held up the cracked water pitcher to Tall Hat.

Again everyone laughed, except Tall Hat. Without a word he took the pitcher and stood looking down at Pino. Then, turning to the boy's father, he said, "The pony is traded to Pino."

Pino was not half a step behind as Tall Hat went over to the corral. He was hanging over the top rail as Tall Hat swung a loop and lassoed the pinto pony. Then Tall Hat put a halter on the pinto and led him over to the boy. Putting the lead rope into Pino's hand he said, "Now he is yours, my friend."

Pino beamed his thanks. When he and his father rode on their way home, the lead rope was still in Pino's hand, and the pony was following.

Pino was very happy. He kept looking back at his pony and thinking what a handsome animal he was and how well he held his head. "I shall call him Paint to myself," Pino thought happily. "For he is a paint pony, and such a fine one, too. I wonder why Tall Hat thought he was loco."

As they drew near Pino's home, he found out.

The pony suddenly decided, with a toss of his head, to stop. And he did! Pino's father's horse, of course, kept right on going. Pino, with the lead rope looped snugly around his waist, sailed through the air and landed ker-flop! right in the dusty road.

A Different Language

Pino picked himself up. He sat there in the dust looking sadly back at the horse. "Now why did you do that, Paint?" he wondered silently.

At that, the pony pricked up his ears and stared at Pino. "Why," the pony thought in surprise, "you can talk!"

Then they both stared at each other. Without either of them speaking a word, they both could understand every word the other thought!

"Imagine a horse being able to talk!" thought Pino.

"Well," thought the pony, "imagine a boy talking like a horse!"

At that moment, Pino's father came out to the road and called back, "Come on, Pino!"

"Get on my back," said the pony. "If anyone is to ride me, it shall be you."

So, to the amazement of his father and mother, Pino rode into the yard sitting easily on the back of the "loco" pony.

"You see," said his father to his mother. "Although the boy cannot speak, he is a natural horseman."

"Your father is right," said the pony, when Pino repeated his father's words to Paint. "For what horseman can talk to his horse as you can?"

From that day on, Pino and Paint were great friends. They were always together. Every afternoon, when Pino had finished helping his mother with pottery, he could hear Paint calling to him.

"Come on, Pino, let's go! I'm tired of standing in the corral all day. Let's go for a ride," Paint would say, though Pino's mother never heard a word.

Then Pino would take a running jump onto his friend's back and away they would go. They visited with prairie dogs on guard at the doorways to their underground cities. They drank together from small, clear, hidden springs. They told each other their thoughts as they jogged homeward in the gold and purple twilight.

On market days, they rode into the settlement. All the men were amazed at the way Pino had tamed down Tall Hat's loco pony. And of course, when Rodeo Day came, and his father and mother rumbled off in the wagon, Pino and Paint went trotting along behind them.

Pino and Paint saw everything there was to see that wonderful day. When the pony race came along they were right beside the track, watching.

"What is this?" Paint asked as the horses formed up at the starting line.

"It's a race," Pino told him. "The big pony race."

"Why aren't we in it, then?" asked Paint. "Hey, move over there!" Paint whinnied to the other ponies. "Make room for us."

To the amazement of everyone, especially the riders, all the horses moved over and made room for Pino and Paint. Then the gun barked. Off they all went!

Down the track they pounded, with dust clouds flying. Pino and Paint were far in the rear, but Paint was getting the feel of the track.

What a thunder of hoofs as the dust clouds whirled! And through it, Pino and Paint edged forward past more and more of the flying feet.

Coming around the last turn, Paint put on a desperate burst of speed. With Pino crouching close to his neck, Paint thundered past the lead horses and up the home stretch.

One last great effort, and Paint had crossed the finish line. Pino and his pony had won the race!

"Paint! We've won!" Pino cried out loud as

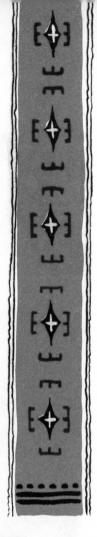

Paint slowed down to a walk, his sides heaving. "We've won!" But Paint said nothing.

"Paint!" cried Pino again. "Can't you hear me?"

Now his father came running alongside, open-mouthed with surprise. He had heard Pino's shouts.

"My son!" he cried. "You can speak!"

Pino, too, was surprised. "Yes," he said, after he had tried again. "I can speak."

But Paint said not a word. He could no longer understand what Pino was saying, now that he talked like other boys. Or perhaps the trouble was that Pino could not understand Paint any more.

At first, when he realized this, Pino felt very sad. But he could see how fine it would be to be able to talk to the other boys and to the men at the agency house.

"And we shall always be friends," Pino whispered to Paint in boy talk as he led the pony back to the judge's stand.

And they are friends to this day. For there is one thing they both still understand—that they like each other.

Up and Down America

America, our country,
Has half a continent,
An ocean for the sun to rise
And one for its descent.
And space for many children
Of different speech and ways,
But standing as one people
In strength and love and praise.

—Dorothy Hall

Comanche and the Fire

Donald and Beth Day

As a young man, Will Rogers worked on his father's ranch. Will's favorite horse was Comanche. Will—or Willie, as he was called then—was more interested in teaching Comanche tricks than he was in his regular cowboy job. Willie's friend Spi, who worked with him, didn't quite understand Willie's attitude.

Willie liked best the mornings when it was his turn to milk and get the water and saddle the horses, instead of cook. It wasn't that Willie liked to get out in the chilly gray early morning and do those chores. He liked it because that way he had a few minutes alone with Comanche before the boys had to get to work.

Comanche could always tell when Willie was coming. He recognized the sound of his walk. When he heard him, Comanche would lift his head and call to Willie—a soft whinny through his nose, as if he were saying, "Good morning, Willie."

Willie would go into the little corral. He would take a little extra time, just fooling with Comanche and talking to him. Comanche couldn't talk, of course, but he would wiggle his ears as though he were listening to Willie.

One morning, Willie took more time with the chores than usual. Spi was in the cabin getting breakfast. He had his biscuit dough all ready for the milk. Willie didn't come with the milk— and he didn't come.

Spi got mad. He started to go out and find Willie, but he just got to the door when his friend came running up. Willie grabbed Spi by the arm. "Come on!" he said. "Come look, Spi!"

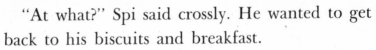

"At what?" Spi said crossly. He wanted to get back to his biscuits and breakfast.

Willie tugged Spi along with him. He was excited and breathless.

"I taught Comanche a trick," he said, "and I want you to see."

When they got to the corral, Comanche was standing there waiting for them. He seemed to know he had done something special. He was ready to show off for Spi.

"All right. What can he do?"

"Watch," said Willie. He stood back, away from the fence, so Comanche could see him. He looked from the horse to the corral gate.

"All right, Comanche," he said softly. "Open the gate!"

Comanche took a step over to the gate. He put his nose under the wooden knob that fitted loosely in a groove. He raised his nose. But the knob didn't lift. Comanche stepped back. He looked puzzled.

"Again, Comanche. Try again," Willie urged the horse.

"Oh, come on and eat breakfast," Spi said.

Willie didn't pay any attention to Spi. He was looking at Comanche, urging him on.

"Open the gate, Comanche," he said. "Try to open the gate."

Comanche tossed his head. Then he walked up to the gate again. He looked at the latch for a minute and lowered his head. He stuck his soft nose tight under and against the wooden knob. He lifted slowly. Snap! The gate fell open.

"Thataboy! Thataboy, Comanche!"

Willie was excited. He patted Comanche's neck and stroked his nose.

"Now can we eat?" Spi asked.

There was a long, hard day's work ahead that day. Willie and Spi came in at noon to the main ranch to change their ponies before they went out to the cattle a few miles from their cabin.

Fire!

In the late afternoon, they were getting ready to quit and go home when they saw something frightening—something that every rancher hates worse than any other sight in the world.

Fire! A long, wavering, smoky line of prairie fire, coming over the horizon.

"Come on!"

It looked quite a long way off, but Willie and Spi hurried toward it. When they got there, men were already busy fighting the fire. All the cowboys and ranchers for miles around had come with wagonloads of water buckets and piles of gunny sacks. They all worked as hard as they could to stop the fire from spreading.

Willie and Spi grabbed sacks, dunked them in water and started working. They slapped and slapped at the creeping flames. They worked till their eyebrows were singed and their clothes were

blackened from the smoke and the scorched grass.

All of a sudden, Willie straightened up. "Spi!" he yelled. "Look!"

Spi looked up. Willie was pointing back over the hill. The line of fire was closing in on their little cabin.

"Comanche!" Willie screamed. "I've got to save Comanche!"

He jumped on the horse nearest him and tore off. Spi followed him. They rode as fast as they could toward their cabin. Tears were running down Willie's cheeks. "I've just got to save Comanche," he kept saying over and over.

Spi didn't say anything, because he didn't think they could save the horse. The fire was running faster than they were.

At last they were close enough to see their cabin and their little corral. But a line of fire separated

them from it. They just could not get through.

Willie rode up as close as he could to the fire. He put his hands to his mouth, and called out.

"Comanche! Comanche! Open the gate, Comanche!"

Through the fire the boys could see the gate of the corral. Inside the fence were their horses.

"Comanche!" Willie called again. "Comanche! Open the gate."

Comanche lifted his ears. He could hear Willie's voice. He took a step toward the gate.

"Hurry, Comanche—open the gate!" Willie kept calling to him. Willie's face was white and scared, and the tears made funny light marks in the dark, smoky dirt on his cheeks.

Comanche twitched his ears. He was listening to Willie. He walked over to the gate and stuck his nose against the knob.

"Come on, Comanche!" Willie begged.

Up. Up again. Then Comanche stepped back. The gate fell open. Comanche walked through. Willie was crying with joy.

"He did it, Spi! He did it! Comanche's out!"

But Spi wasn't as happy as Willie. He was

looking at his own pony. His pony was still inside the corral, even though the gate was open. The pony was frightened and he kept whirling around in a circle. He didn't try to get out. He didn't seem to know what to do.

Comanche looked back at the corral and saw the other pony still inside the fence. Quickly he turned back and raced inside the corral. He jumped at the other pony, and kicked at him. He nipped him and fought him. The pony forgot about being frightened. He kicked back at Comanche and then he raced out of the corral. Comanche raced after him. In a couple of minutes they were both way out on the range where it was green and safe, and free from the terrible threat of fire.

Willie was so proud of Comanche he could hardly speak. He tried to say something and it got all choked in his throat.

After a few minutes, and a few swallows, he got his voice back. He took Spi's arm. "Guess we better get back to our fire-fighting," he whispered. "We don't need to worry about anything here— not with Comanche looking after things."

A Trip to Lancaster Market

Marguerite deAngeli

Lydia, a little Pennsylvania German girl, had been promised a trip to the Lancaster market by her father, Henner. To go on the trip, she had to finish a hooked mat she was making. Lydia finished the mat, but carelessly left it out in the rain! To be careless —"shusselie"—was about the worst thing a little Pennsylvania German girl could be.

Early the next morning, Mother came up very quietly to wake Lydia. She took hold of her shoulder gently and said, "Ssh! When you come down, make shut the door so Nancy sleeps!"

The rain had stopped. The sun wasn't up yet, of course, for this was market day. Baking must be done for Sunday. All the chores must be attended to. The things for market must be put in the wagon.

It was very cold again. Lydia didn't feel much like getting up, especially when she thought about her mat. But she wouldn't think of not obeying. Dressing in the half-dark, she slipped quietly out the door.

Mom had breakfast well on the way. The kitchen was full of the smell of good things. Malinda was putting a clean white cloth over a basket. The basket was filled with rolls of fresh butter and crocks of cottage cheese. The end of the table was loaded with things to go in the back of the wagon.

Pop came in and hung his hat on the peg. "Well, Lyddy," he said, whisking her up off the floor.

Lydia couldn't bear to tell him that she couldn't go after all, because she had been so "shusselie," and had left her mat out in the rain. Before she could think what to tell him, Pop said, "I guess your mat makes dry, think, Mom? When we come home, I go by the arbor to see if Malinda makes the chicken house door fast. The lantern makes a light on your mat, Lyddy. *It* lies out on the bench still. So, I thinks, 'That Lyddy, she's a shussle!' But I bring in the mat and make dry by the stove."

"Oh, Pop!" Lydia wriggled down and ran to the stove room. She found the mat all safe. But when she brought it to the light, her heart sank! Sure enough, the pink had run into the lighter

pink in the middle of the roses so that they looked smudgy. Now she could never sell it.

Mom said, "Yes, well." She went back to the stove to her cooking.

Malinda said, "You know, I like it so. It looks more soft that way!"

Pop just stood a minute, looking at the mat and then at poor Lydia. She was feeling pretty sorry just then. "Nice it looks, Lyddy, and makes good and warm by your bed, ain't? The edge iss not so straight anyways. But you finish, so!" Pop's eyes twinkled at Lydia.

"You mean I can go?"

"Sure! But make quick! Look, by the clock I should be gone already." They all sat down to breakfast.

Mother didn't go to market because she had too many other things to do. Malinda had to stay home and help too.

Lydia scurried up the stairs. She changed her apron and put on her bonnet and shawl. By the time she came down, Pop was ready to start. It was daylight. The sun was just beginning to show over the blue hills.

Lydia sat close to Father on the seat of the Germantown wagon. It was chilly riding through the mists that lay in the low places. But oh! it was fun to be going to Lancaster! And perhaps she could make another mat—quickly, this time—and sell it to buy Mom's present.

By the time Henner and Lydia reached Lancaster there were many wagons and carriages and cars on the road. Many greetings were exchanged. They had to find a place for the market wagon. They had to get the things onto the counters in the stall.

The big Lancaster market has rows and rows

of stalls, or little booths with counters, where the farmers bring all kinds of things to sell. Lydia arranged the chickens in neat rows. They were all cleaned and ready to cook. Then she put the little pots of cheese and pots of butter in rows. Mother had sent a few jars of homemade pickles and jellies, too. Lydia had some parsley to tuck in here and there. It all looked so delicious!

People began to come in to buy, and everybody had a smile for Lydia. Pop let Lydia do most of the selling. She was having a wonderful time! Pop wrapped up the packages. But he let Lydia take the money and helped her make change.

"By Jacob Zook's"

Lydia began to get hungry. She had been so excited she hadn't eaten enough breakfast. Pop said, "Not much left to sell. I stay by the apple butter awhile. You go by Jacob Zook's store and get you something. I'll come along. Here! This is for a smart helper."

He handed Lydia twenty-five cents! She said, "Ooh!" That was more money than Lydia had ever had! Now she could buy a present for Mom.

Lydia started out in the direction Pop had told her to go. She went gaily up one aisle of the market and down another. She passed stalls filled with dressed turkeys and chickens and ducks.

There were so many women with market baskets on their arms that Lydia could hardly manage to get through to the door. She came out on the street, but it didn't look just as she expected it would! She had gone out the back door instead of the front!

Lydia looked up and down the street. It really was just an alley. She hurried to the corner, where she saw many people passing. She was sure this must be the street where Jacob Zook's lunch place was. Father had told her it was just out the door and around the corner.

There were many fascinating things in the shop windows. Lydia stopped to look. One window was filled with toys such as Lydia had never seen. Another window was in a hardware store. It was

filled with tools of all kinds. One window had a display of food. Not homemade food—"boughten" food!

The food made her hungry again, and she began to look around for Jacob Zook's store. It was nowhere to be seen! Lydia turned and turned, she looked and looked. But at every turn she became more confused.

She walked along a little farther. No sign could she see that said, "Jacob Zook, Quick Lunch." What is more, she couldn't even see the market.

Lydia's chin began to quiver. She didn't want to cry, but she felt very much alone. The people went hurrying by as if they knew just where they were going. They didn't even see a lonely little girl in a blue dress and a black bonnet.

Suddenly she heard, "Ya, vell. So here you are, already!"

She looked up. And there was Pop! Never had she been so glad to see him. Lydia took hold of his hand and held on tight. Pop led her around a corner. There was Jacob Zook's. It had been right there all the time!

"Now, up you go!" Pop lifted Lydia up onto the

high stool. Lydia sighed with delight. She was really going to have a "store" dinner. Ice cream, maybe!

Jacob said, "Ah, your Lyddy, Henner, ain't? She gets a big girl, now!"

Henner joked with Jacob, and they talked about the weather, about the crops, about everything.

Lydia finished eating and wished they could go to look in the stores, or maybe "shuss" through some bargains. Perhaps she could find a present for Mom.

Henner finished and paid for his dinner and Lydia's. Lydia looked up as her father took her hand and they left Jacob Zook's. "Could I maybe buy a present for Mom?"

"Ya, a piece of goods gives a nice present for Mom, ain't? Let's go by Himmelreich's."

Lydia skipped along by Pop's side. Now she was happy.

They picked out a piece of the very finest lawn for Mom to use for her caps. Lyddy's twenty-five cents helped to pay for it. Then they went back to the market place, got into the wagon, and started home.

Chi-wee and the Pinyon Nuts

Grace Moon

Chi-wee felt very lonely that day. There seemed no one to play with, in all the pueblo. The little girl stood on the edge of the mesa and looked away into the great sweep of desert where the wind was playing tag with the little white-tailed hares. She could smell the odor of distant rain and could see the clouds piling up in white bunches behind the faint blue hills.

"Come, Chi-wee, little daughter," called a voice. Chi-wee turned and walked slowly back into her one-room home where her mother sat drawing designs on pottery jars.

"The wind blew cold from the north last night. Do you not think so, little daughter?" her mother asked without looking up.

"Yes," nodded Chi-wee. "It was cold, my mother."

"Do you think there was frost, Chi-wee?"

"Yes," answered the little girl again. "There was frost in the house shadows before the sun came up, my mother."

Her mother glanced up. "Could you reach the pinyon trees and return before dark, little one?"

Then did Chi-wee open her eyes wide and throw back her head. Always the first frost opened the pinyon cones and loosened the delicious little nuts. And the pinyon trees were out in the desert on the edge of the large arroyo.

"May I go, my mother?" cried Chi-wee. "I will fill my basket, the big one, with the choicest of all the nuts. Oh, may I go *now?*"

"Yes—go, little daughter," said the mother. "And see that you are back before the night chill comes."

Down the trail Chi-wee danced. Past rocks and sharp turns she ran. Now she could feel the desert wind in her face.

It was quite a distance to the pinyon trees on the arroyo, but it did not take Chi-wee very long to reach them. Sure enough, she found some of the nuts on the ground. When she threw rocks up into the branches, more fell. She ate a few. They tasted more delicious than ever before. But there would be plenty of time to gather the nuts.

How clean the arroyo looked, and what a lovely place to run! She looked at the steep, sandy sides. It was very easy to get down. All she had to do was to start and the sand did the rest. She slid straight to the bottom and found herself standing on the clean white floor. It looked like what it really was—the bed of a stream in the time of rains, but very dry now.

How firm it felt, and how cool and pleasant.

Chi-wee threw back her head and ran like a deer. She did not know that, as she ran, a tiny pool of water lay in each footprint that she left!

On she ran—and on—and on—until finally she stopped, panting for breath, and looked for a place to rest. A twisted old pinyon tree grew right out of the arroyo's side about a third of the way up.

Chi-wee scrambled with some difficulty up into its branches. She stretched her small length on the welcome trunk. It just seemed to fit her. How quiet it was here, and how beautiful—and how tired she was—. Slowly her eyes grew drowsy. She slipped off into a delicious sleep.

It seemed to Chi-wee that she just closed her eyes and opened them again. But what strange thing had happened so suddenly?

It was growing dark now, and very cold. Above her was sky, gray and soft. Below her was sky, but cold wind, too, and noise. The below-sky was moving—swiftly, with a rushing sound! And suddenly she knew! It was *water!* It had rained in the distant hills. The arroyo was a wide, wild stream!

She could not go down again, that was plain.

But she must climb up and go home quickly, for her mother would be having anxious thoughts.

It was growing darker now. As Chi-wee looked at the sandy bank above her, her little heart sank. For it curved *in,* offering no hand or foot-hold. Chi-wee tried several times to climb up the bank, but only slipped back the few feet she could go.

She was sobbing now, quietly to herself. She put her hands over her face and lay in the tree, trying to think what to do. The sky turned grayer still. The sun left a narrow streak of red as it sank.

Then, suddenly, Chi-wee heard a sound—and sat up in her tree, listening. At first she could not tell what it was. Then she knew it must be some-one singing, someone very near!

Chi-wee cried out as loud as she could. The singing stopped. And then, suddenly, right above her, was a face looking into her own. Farther over the edge came the head. Chi-wee saw that it was a boy—a Navajo boy, a little older than herself.

"I fell asleep in the tree and the waters came," called Chi-wee. "Is there a way, Navajo boy, that you can get me out?"

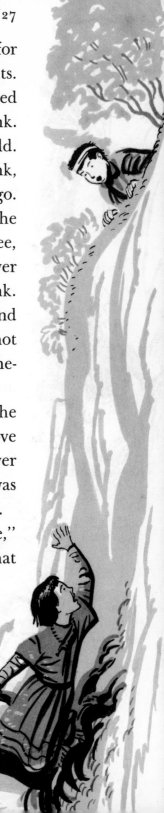

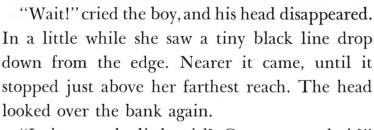

"Wait!" cried the boy, and his head disappeared. In a little while she saw a tiny black line drop down from the edge. Nearer it came, until it stopped just above her farthest reach. The head looked over the bank again.

"Is it enough, little girl? Can you reach it?" he cried.

"No," answered Chi-wee, in disappointment.

"Wait!" he called again, and drew the line back. In a little while it came again. This time the strong hide thong crept closer. Chi-wee finally caught hold of it and wrapped it about both wrists.

"Do not put all your weight on the thong," called the boy. "Climb with your feet and hold to the line."

Chi-wee did not need this advice. Very soon she was up on the arroyo bank unwrapping the thong from her wrists.

The boy was very gentle. He carefully rubbed the red lines on her wrists that the thong had made. He pushed her down into a seat of springy sage. "You must have hunger," he said quietly. He took from a little pouch at his belt some dried goat's meat and a seed cake. Oh, how good they tasted to Chi-wee!

"You are from the mesa?" asked the boy.

"Yes," answered Chi-wee. "And my mother will have very anxious thoughts for me." Then her eyes opened very wide.

"But look!" she cried. "We are on the away side of the wash!"

It was true, and for a moment the boy frowned in thought. "Come," he said. "I know a place not so wide. Let us go quickly while we can see."

They walked quickly. In a little while the boy cried out, "This is the place."

The water had washed the sand away from the roots of a large juniper tree. It had fallen right

across the water and made a tree bridge across the stream. The boy walked across it easily. But Chi-wee could not make her feet go across.

"Oh, I cannot," cried Chi-wee. "I will fall into the water!"

The boy laughed at that. He came back across the tree and held out his hand. Little by little, he led her across the shaky bridge. At the last she gave a jump and landed in a heap on the right side of the arroyo!

"Oh, it is good to be on this side!" she cried. "You have helped me very much."

"I take care of sheep for my mother," he said. "We live over there, on the edge of the desert." And Chi-wee could see a tiny line of gray smoke rising from some cottonwood trees, and a little light that shone there.

"I come often here, with my sheep," said the boy. "Will you come again?"

A happy feeling came into Chi-wee's heart then.

"Oh, yes," she said. "Oh, yes, I shall come to this place." And she ran toward the mesa with the speed of the wind. She could come again for pinyon nuts. And she had found a new friend!

When Glory Went
To Peddle Pine

May Justus

*Glory and her brother Matt lived
with Mammy and Grandy, in a cabin
on Kettle Creek, somewhere in the
mountains of the South. Glory had
never been on the other side of the
mountain, to the little settlement
called Slab Town.*

Shortly after New Year's Day, there was a spell
of good weather. The sun shone out and melted
the snow. It melted the ice in Kettle Creek. It
crept into the chimney corner where Grandy had
spent so many days. Even old Barney, lying in the
sun, wagged his tail more blithely.

Glory and Matt were busy. They had a grand
plan for peddling pine. The horse, Moses, would
draw the little two-wheeled cart which Matt and
Grandy had fashioned. This cart, made from two
wagon wheels and some boards from an old barn

floor, was sturdy enough to go over the trail. But the trail had first to be cleared. Matt grubbed up bushes. Glory carried off sticks and stones.

"Now I can drive to Slab Town with a load of kindling," said Matt.

"Now *we* can drive," said Glory. "I am going to drive with you. I have always wanted to see how it looks on the other side of the mountain."

Matt agreed. There was nothing else to do, for Moses belonged to Glory. In the end, he accepted her as a partner, giving her a share in his cart for a share in Moses.

One afternoon, they bundled pine and packed the cart for the journey. That night, Glory could hardly sleep for thinking about it. She dreamed at last of sitting on a stack of pine as high as a mountain, and driving down Kettle Creek until the cart wheels made a noise like thunder.

Mammy had breakfast ready for them: bacon and grits and gravy. "Eat all you can," she told them. "It will warm you up for your trip."

When the time came to go, she put a hot stone in the cart to warm their feet. "Good-bye! Take good care of yourselves. Get back before night."

Then, with a clatter and a creak, the cart started down the mountain. The early morning air stung Glory's cheeks. It nipped the ends of her fingers through her thick yarn gloves. But her heart felt warm within her. At last—at last she was on her way to the other side of the mountain!

The trail went into the creek-bed road, which they followed for a long way. Then they rounded the mountain and entered the valley.

"Are we almost there?" Glory asked.

Matt laughed. "Why, we've barely started. It will take us a long, long time to get to Slab Town."

"Oh, goody!" Glory cried. "I should like to sit up here with you and ride all day."

The sun was over the mountaintop now, and the air was warmer. Glory thought that the world had never looked so beautiful. Everyone they met seemed glad to see them. She said, "Howdy!" to everyone who spoke. Sometimes they met a team and its driver, sometimes a man or boy going to the mill. Glory began whistling the lively air of an old-time song.

"There you go!" Matt reproved her. "Whistling like a tomboy!"

"Miss Penny whistled," said Glory calmly, "lots better than Grandy or you. If I keep on practicing, I might do as well some day." By and by she sang the words that went with the tune.

When I was a little boy I lived by myself.
All the bread and cheese I got I put upon a shelf.
To my wing-wong waddle, to my jackstraw saddle,
To my John far-faddle, to my long ways home!

A mighty roar drowned out the last of this song.

"Oh, Matt, what is it?" cried Glory, throwing her hands over her ears.

Matt drew Moses to a standstill. "A train is coming," he told her. "Yonder is the railroad track, where the sun shines on the rails."

The engine appeared with a terrible roar. It dashed around the curve of the mountain, a long line of cars rumbling after it. Then it was gone.

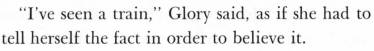

"I've seen a train," Glory said, as if she had to tell herself the fact in order to believe it.

Soon they were in Slab Town. It seemed a wonderful place, with tall brick chimneys rising from houses two stories high. Most of these houses were gray or brown, but here and there was a white one. All had neat little picket fences.

Adventure in Slab Town

"Just think," said Glory wonderingly. "Just think, Matt. The folks who live here get to see the train go by every day!"

"If you'll stay here and keep the wagon," said Matt, "you may get to see another one pass. I will take some kindling across to those houses and see if I can sell it."

Glory took the reins in her sturdy hands and held them steadily. Matt gathered up an armful of kindling and hurried across the tracks. She passed the time by looking at all the houses and by counting the glass windows in them. So many windows! The people in those houses could see the world outside them on the coldest winter days!

A train came chugging down the tracks. Glory

felt helpless and frightened. It seemed as if the iron monster were bearing down upon her. Old Moses trembled. Without warning, he bolted madly forward. Glory held the lines as well as she could. Oh, if Matt were only here! But Matt was nowhere in sight.

As they sped down the road by the side of the track, Glory pulled the lines still harder. Moses came to a stop just opposite the engine.

A fat man stuck his head out and asked, "What's the matter there—a runaway?"

Poor Glory was still so badly frightened that she couldn't speak to save her life. The fat man left his engine and came over to the little cart.

"Poor child!" he said kindly. "What are you doing here, anyway? And what's all this jumbled up in the back of your wagon?"

"Pine," replied Glory, swallowing hard. She had been so afraid that the kindling would be thrown out as they tore along. But it seemed to be safe in the wagon. "We brought it to sell," she explained to the fat man.

"Who is 'we?'" he asked her. "You and your horse, I suppose."

"There's Matt, too," she told him. "He went across the railroad to see if he could sell some kindling."

The fat man picked up a bundle of pine. "How do you sell it?"

"Ten cents for the little bundles—twenty-five cents for the big ones."

"Pretty good kindling," remarked the man. "I'll just take all you have here. Then I'll have about enough to do me the rest of the winter."

As he spoke, he gathered up a big load and took it back to his engine. Another man came and carried a load. Then the cart was empty. The fat man

took out a pocketbook and handed Glory some money. There were one—two—three—four—five green bills and several small pieces of silver.

"That's a lot of money. Isn't it too much?" Glory asked him.

The fat man shook his head and laughed. "There's just a little bit extra. That's the silver, and it's your own, to make up for my scaring you so and because you're a brave young lady." Then he took off his cap, made a bow to her, and went back to his engine. Glory called, "Thank you!" after him.

Just then she heard the sound of running feet. Glancing back, she saw Matt coming. He looked rather cross, and called as he came, "What have you been doing?"

"Selling the kindling," she replied. Matt still had a bundle of kindling in his arms. That meant that he hadn't sold it. He looked and saw that the cart was empty.

"Where is the kindling?" he asked her. He seemed unable to believe that Glory had really sold it.

"Over in the engine," she explained. "A fat man bought all of it. See the money he gave me for it." Matt whistled his amazement.

"The silver is mine," Glory said. "But I will divide it with you, because you got scared a little bit, too. At least, you looked like it."

They went to a store together, after tying old Moses so he wouldn't get loose and bolt in another runaway. There were several purchases to make—flour, salt, coffee, and sugar. While Matt attended to these, Glory looked all about her.

What attracted her most of all was the candy. So many kinds, so many shapes, so many gay

colors! Some of the pieces had little stick handles. These, Matt explained, were to hold while one nibbled the other end. They were called "all-day suckers."

"I want some of those," Glory told Matt. After she bought the candy, they went out to find Moses. Then they got in the two-wheeled cart and started back home.

It took much longer to get back home than the trip had taken that morning. There were steep places to climb. Moses had to rest often. Before they came to the end of the trail, the early twilight had fallen. The smoke of many supper fires was curling up to the sky.

Barney barked a joyous welcome from the cabin door. Mammy and Grandy came out and asked, "Did you have any luck today?"

"Lots of luck—good luck!" Glory answered. And she told what had happened. Then she gave Mammy and Grandy an all-day sucker apiece. Mammy chose a yellow one, and Grandy chose a red.

Town Moose

Phil Stong

A big moose scared the Minnesota town of Birora by moving into Mr. Ketonen's livery stable. But Ivar, Mr. Ketonen's son, and his friends Waino and Jim were fond of the moose, which they named Honk. The boys were unhappy when Mr. Ketonen tried to shut the moose out.

The boys reached the stable about four o'clock and found the big front doors closed. When they had gone through the small door in the big door, there was no one in the stable but the horses.

Jim Barry laughed. "We can let him right in."

Ivar shook his head. "Papa would know."

They sat around and thought for a while. Then Ivar had an idea. He whispered it. Then he said, "The park would be the best place. Nobody goes there in the winter."

There were lots of fat boys in Birora, but in five minutes three of the fattest boys that had ever been seen anywhere slipped out of the *back* door of the livery stable. About ten minutes later, the same three fat boys came out again—and in ten minutes, again.

They walked very curiously, waddling almost, in single file like Indians. Every once in a while the front fat boy, Ivar, would dodge behind a tree. The others would dodge behind trees. At last they crept into safety among the trees of the city park.

In another five minutes Ivar, Waino, and Jim— thin boys now—came up to the *front* doors of the stable. "You know him best," Jim whispered. "You wait for him and we'll—?"

In five minutes only *two* of the fattest boys that had ever been seen crept out of the back door.

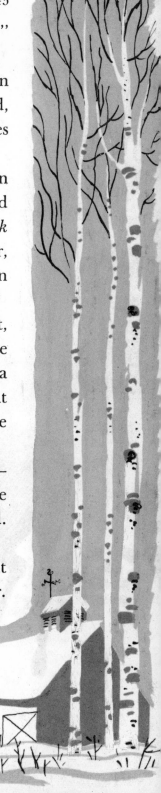

Ivar was very uneasy. He didn't seem *very* fat now, but Papa would be sure to notice. "Oh, come on, moose."

"Oh, come *on,* moose—come on, good old Honk!"

"Haawwnnkk!"

Ivar peered around the corner and saw Honk. "Thank goodness! You're awful late." Ivar reached under his Mackinaw and pulled out a big handful of hay. "Come on, Honk."

By deserted back streets, he led the animal down toward the park with its nailed-up band-

stand. The wind was bitter cold. But Honk didn't mind that. What Honk minded was never being able to get more than a nibble of hay at a time. The little thing holding the hay would run, and then would hold out another nibble of hay.

Then Honk went into another of those flat tree things—it was the small room under the band-stand where they kept hoses and rakes and things for the park. And there was a great deal of loose grass and the other two little things who could almost speak Moose.

He liked the loose grass. He liked the three little

things that were always around it. He ate a long time. But he wasn't sleepy. When the three little things decided to leave, he didn't like it.

"HAAAWWWNNNKKK!"

Ivar turned on him. "Oh, my goodness, Honk!"

"You'll have the whole town down on us," Waino said.

Honk was quiet as soon as they came back. "You've got to keep quiet, you old moose! You don't know what would happen to you if they caught you down here." Ivar gave Honk a prod in the ribs, which Honk accepted as a specially friendly pat.

The boys were growing a little upset. It was supper time. Their mothers would be waiting.

They tried once more to slip out together, but Honk had begun to grow more and more fond of the little things. Just as Ivar went out the door, Honk said, a good deal more loudly than before, "HAWWWWNNNNKKKK." For him it was warm under the bandstand, out of the wind. He couldn't see why these little grass things would want to go out in the cold either.

"Now listen, Honk!" Ivar argued. "Our folks

are waiting for us. You stay here quiet and maybe we can come down a minute after supper."

Honk knew no English. His only reply was a pleased "Hawwnnkk" or two as the boys returned.

"Am I going to catch it when I get home!" Jim Barry said.

"I'll tell you," Ivar said generously. "Honk knows Waino and me better than he knows you. You see if you can get away. If you can, Waino can try it. Then I'll sneak out somehow."

"Well—if you think you can manage him," Jim

said, rather guiltily. He slid out of the bandstand. While Jim was leaving, Ivar poked Honk in the ribs several times as hard as he could. He had learned that Honk liked this. The moose did indeed. He paid no attention to Jim.

"Well, that's one of us out," Ivar said. "You're behind him, Waino. You better get away while you can." Ivar was scratching the moose's neck with both hands. Honk had turned his head and was looking at the boy with two sad, soft eyes— like two cups of beef broth.

"I'll wait for you outside," Waino said. He slid out. The moose kept on gazing at Ivar.

Ivar's hands grew tired. At last he got down on the floor and scratched together a little pile of hay. He pushed this off toward the side of the moose away from the door.

The Getaway

"Here's a bite you missed, Honk," he said very kindly. Then he slid out into the darkness. Waino was waiting for him. The two boys stood for a moment listening. There was nothing but the sound of chewing.

"Let's get out of here," said Ivar. They stole very slowly and carefully away.

At last they got to the sidewalk and started off briskly. They would just have time to stop at the livery stable before running home to their suppers.

They had gotten clear down to the main street before they noticed that the few people on the street were acting oddly. They were all going indoors. An automobile that had been coming toward them suddenly turned up on the sidewalk. It backed quickly with a rasp of gears and dashed back the way it had come. A miner that they knew waved his arms at them, opened his mouth to shout, and then turned and ran.

"What's the matter with them?" Waino asked.

"Guess they can't stand the cold," Ivar said scornfully.

They could stand the cold. They threw back their shoulders and strutted down the street and around the corner to the livery stable. Ivar's father and the town councilmen were sitting in the office, very much pleased with themselves.

"Well, I guess we got rid of him, all right," Ivar's father was saying for about the twentieth time.

"I guess we did," the Mayor said. "Of course, if it had been safe, it might have been a good thing to keep him. A tame moose! Lots of summer people might have come up to see him."

At this moment Ivar and Waino entered. Because he felt a little guilty, Ivar thought he should say something very innocent. "We're going right to supper, Papa. We didn't see how late it was."

"All right, son. You'd better hurry—"

Ivar's father quit talking then and his mouth fell open. The councilmen turned. All of their mouths fell open, making five open mouths in all. And then, at last, Ivar and Waino turned. And there were seven mouths open.

"Haawwnnkk!" said Honk, as much as to say, "Why did you run off from me?" And he curled his neck around for Ivar to scratch.

"Well, I'll be frostbitten!" said the Mayor. "Put him in a stall, Ivar, where he'll be safe. I guess this town is going to have a moose whether it wants one or not."

Words With Wings

Some words are steeds with silver wings.
  Some words will never fly:
They plod, poor grubby earthbound things,
  And never reach the sky.

But if winged words you chance to see,
  Steal up and clamber on—
And with the poem suddenly
  Go soaring to the sun.

—*Dorothy Hall*

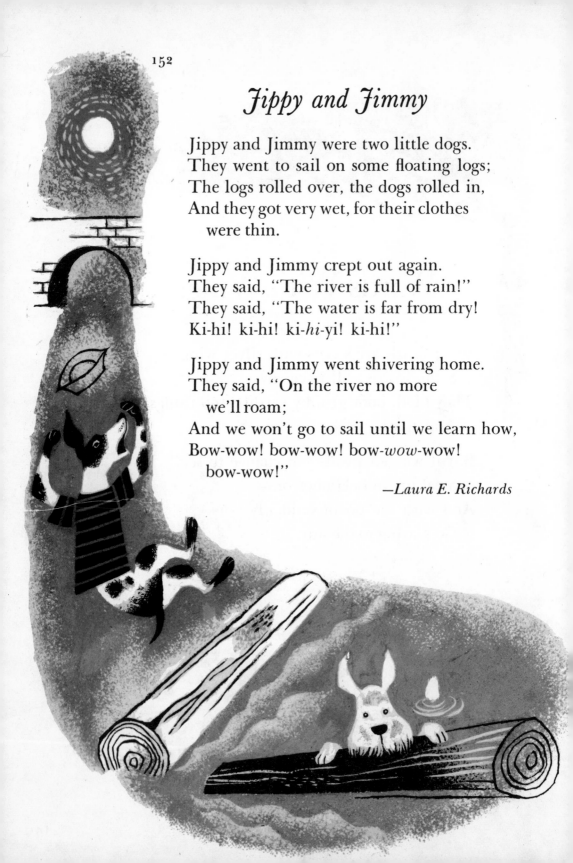

Jippy and Jimmy

Jippy and Jimmy were two little dogs.
They went to sail on some floating logs;
The logs rolled over, the dogs rolled in,
And they got very wet, for their clothes
   were thin.

Jippy and Jimmy crept out again.
They said, "The river is full of rain!"
They said, "The water is far from dry!
Ki-hi! ki-hi! ki-*hi*-yi! ki-hi!"

Jippy and Jimmy went shivering home.
They said, "On the river no more
   we'll roam;
And we won't go to sail until we learn how,
Bow-wow! bow-wow! bow-*wow*-wow!
   bow-wow!"

                    —*Laura E. Richards*

The Hairy Dog

My dog's so furry I've not seen
His face for years and years:
His eyes are buried out of sight,
I only guess his ears.

When people ask me for his breed,
I do not know or care:
He has the beauty of them all
Hidden beneath his hair.

—*Herbert Asquith*

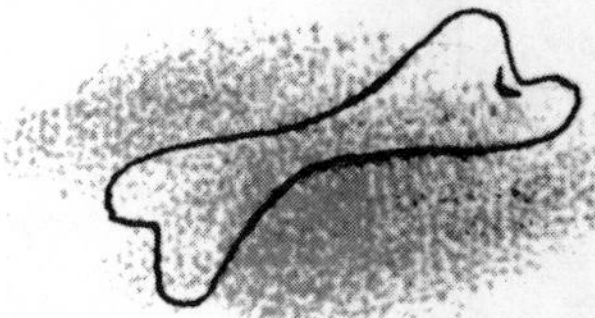

Billy Goats Chew

The billy goat would like to chew
Your picture book or shirt or shoe.
He eats the laundry off the line.
He likes the taste of sticks and twine.
His whiskers wiggle on his chin.
He doesn't *really* swallow *tin*.
The nanny goat is billy's bride.
They chew the laundry side by side.

—*Richard W. Emery*

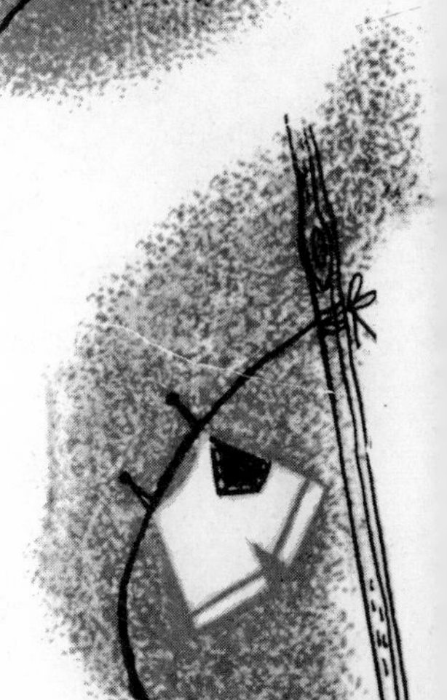

Flying Kite

I often sit and wish that I
Could be a kite up in the sky,
And ride upon the breeze and go
Whatever way it chanced to blow;
Then I could look beyond the town,
And see the river winding down,
And follow all the ships that sail
Like me before the merry gale,
Until at last with them I came
To some place with a foreign name.

—*Frank Dempster Sherman*

The Pasture

I'm going out to clean the pasture spring;
I'll only stop to rake the leaves away
(And wait to watch the water clear, I may):
I shan't be gone long.—You come too.

I'm going out to fetch the little calf
That's standing by the mother. It's so young
It totters when she licks it with her tongue.
I shan't be gone long.—You come too.

—*Robert Frost*

Roads

A road might lead to anywhere—
To harbor towns and quays,
Or to a witch's pointed house
Hidden by bristly trees.

It might lead past the tailor's door
Where he sews with needle and thread,
Or by Miss Pim, the milliner's,
With her hats for every head.

It might be a road to a great, dark cave
With treasure and gold piled high,
Or a road with a mountain tied to its end,
Blue-humped against the sky.

Oh, a road might lead you anywhere—
To Mexico or Maine.
But then, it might just fool you, and—
Lead you back home again!

—*Rachel Field*

The Monkeys and the Crocodile

Five little monkeys
   Swinging from a tree;
Teasing Uncle Crocodile,
   Merry as can be.
Swinging high, swinging low,
   Swinging left and right:
"Dear Uncle Crocodile,
   Come and take a bite!"

Five little monkeys
   Swinging in the air;
Heads up, tails up,
   Little do they care.
Swinging up, swinging down,
   Swinging far and near:
"Poor Uncle Crocodile,
   Aren't you hungry, dear?"

Four little monkeys
   Sitting in the tree;
Heads down, tails down,
   Dreary as can be.
Weeping loud, weeping low,
   Crying to each other:
"Wicked Uncle Crocodile,
   To gobble up our brother!"

          —*Laura E. Richards*

The Sea Gull

The sea gull curves his wings,
The sea gull turns his eyes.
Get down into the water, fish!
(If you are wise.)

The sea gull slants his wings,
The sea gull turns his head.
Get down into the water, fish!
(Or you'll be dead.)

          —*Elizabeth Coatsworth*

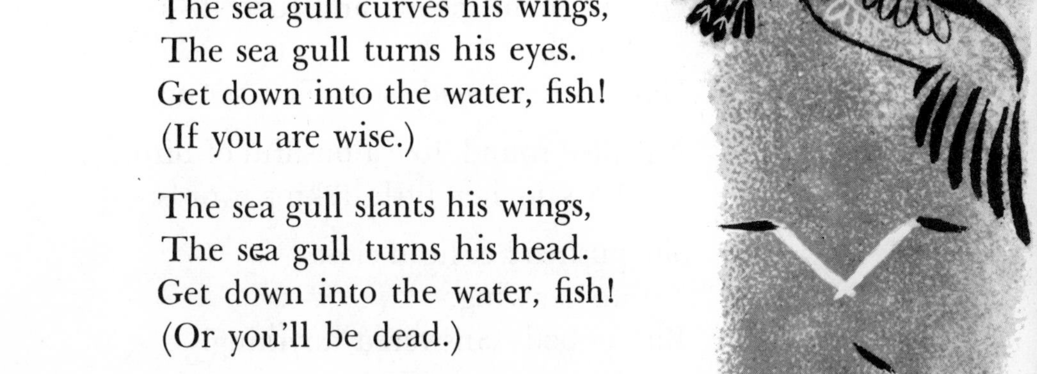

The Hens

The night was coming very fast;
It reached the gate as I ran past.

The pigeons had gone to the tower
   of the church
And all the hens were on their perch,

Up in the barn, and I thought I heard
A piece of a little purring word.

I stopped inside, waiting and staying,
To try to hear what the hens
    were saying.

They were asking something,
   that was plain,
Asking it over and over again.

One of them moved and turned
   around,
Her feathers made a ruffled sound,

A ruffled sound, like a bushful of birds,
As she said her little asking words.

She pushed her head close
   into her wing.
But nobody answered anything.

—*Elizabeth Madox Roberts*

Trot Along, Pony

Trot along, pony.
  Late in the day,
Down by the meadow
  Is the loveliest way.

The apples are rosy
  And ready to fall.
The branches hang over
  By Grandfather's wall.

But the red sun is sinking
  Away out of sight.
The chickens are settling
  Themselves for the night.

Your stable is waiting
  And supper will come.
So turn again, pony,
  Turn again home.

—Marion Edey and Dorothy Grider

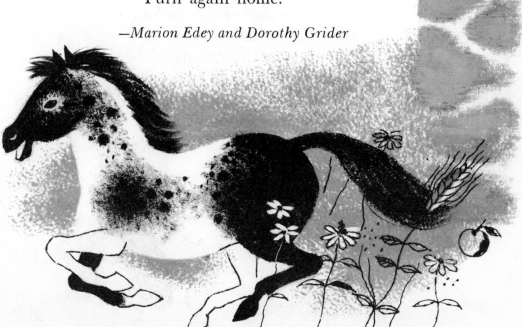

The Little Rose Tree

Every rose on the little tree
Is making a different face at me!
Some look surprised when I pass by,
And others droop—but they are shy.
These two whose heads together press
Tell secrets I could never guess.
Some have their heads thrown back
   to sing,
And all the buds are listening.
I wonder if the gardener knows,
Or if he calls each just a rose?

—*Rachel Field*

A Bird Came Down the Walk

A bird came down the walk:
He did not know I saw;
He bit an angle-worm in halves
And ate the fellow, raw.
And then he drank a dew.
From a convenient grass,
And then hopped sidewise to the wall
To let a beetle pass.

—*Emily Dickinson*

Early Crocus

A chubby little crocus,
A nubby little crocus,
A fubby little crocus
Peeked up to see the sun,
Before the cold was over,
Beside a sleepy clover,
It looked the garden over—
Before the snow was done.

A little snowbird spied it
And for a moment eyed it,
Then settled down beside it
And said (I *think*): "Oh, dear,
I hope you brought your mittens
And furs, like willow-kittens,
Or you'll get chilled to bittens
So early in the year."

—*Aileen Fisher*

The Best Game the Fairies Play

The best game the fairies play,
  The best game of all,
Is sliding down steeples—
  (You know they're very tall).
You fly to the weathercock,
  And when you hear it crow
You fold your wings and clutch
    your things
  And then let go!

They have a million other games—
  Cloud-catching's one,
And mud-mixing after rain
  Is heaps and heaps of fun;
But when you go and stay with them
  Never mind the rest,
Take my advice—they're very nice,
  But steeple-sliding's best!

—*Rose Fyleman*

Some One

Some one came knocking
   At my wee, small door;
Some one came knocking,
   I'm sure—sure—sure;
I listened, I opened,
   I looked to left and right,
But nought there was a-stirring
   In the still dark night;
Only the busy beetle
   Tap-tapping in the wall,
Only from the forest
   The screech-owl's call,
Only the cricket whistling
   While the dewdrops fall,
So I know not who came knocking,
   At all, at all, at all.

             —*Walter de la Mare*

Jonathan Bing

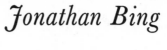

Poor old Jonathan Bing
Went out in his carriage to visit the King,
But everyone pointed and said, "Look at that!
Jonathan Bing has forgotten his hat!"
(He'd forgotten his hat!)

Poor old Jonathan Bing
Went home and put on a new hat for the King.
But up by the palace a soldier said, "Hi!
You can't see the King; you've forgotten
    your tie!"
(He'd forgotten his tie!)

Poor old Jonathan Bing,
He put on a *beautiful* tie for the King,
But when he arrived, an Archbishop said, "Ho!
You can't come to court in pajamas,
    you know!"

Poor old Jonathan Bing
Went home and addressed a short note
    to the King:
    "If you please will excuse me
    I won't come to tea;
    For home's the best place for
    All people like me!"

—*B. Curtis Brown*

Miss T.

It's a very odd thing—
   As odd as can be—
That whatever Miss T. eats
   Turns into Miss T.;
Porridge and apples,
   Mince, muffins and mutton,
Jam, junket, jumbles—
   Not a rap, not a button
It matters; the moment
   They're out of her plate,
Though shared by Miss Butcher
   And sour Mr. Bate;
Tiny and cheerful,
   And neat as can be,
Whatever Miss T. eats
   Turns into Miss T.

—Walter de la Mare

Wind Is a Cat

Wind is a cat
  That prowls at night,
Now in a valley,
  Now on a height,

Pouncing on houses
  Till folks in their beds
Draw all the covers
  Over their heads.

It sings to the moon,
  It scratches at doors;
It lashes its tail
  Around chimneys and roars.

It claws at the clouds
  Till it fringes their silk,
It laps up the dawn
  Like a saucer of milk;

Then, chasing the stars
  To the tops of the firs,
Curls down for a nap
  And purrs and purrs.

               —*Ethel Romig Fuller*

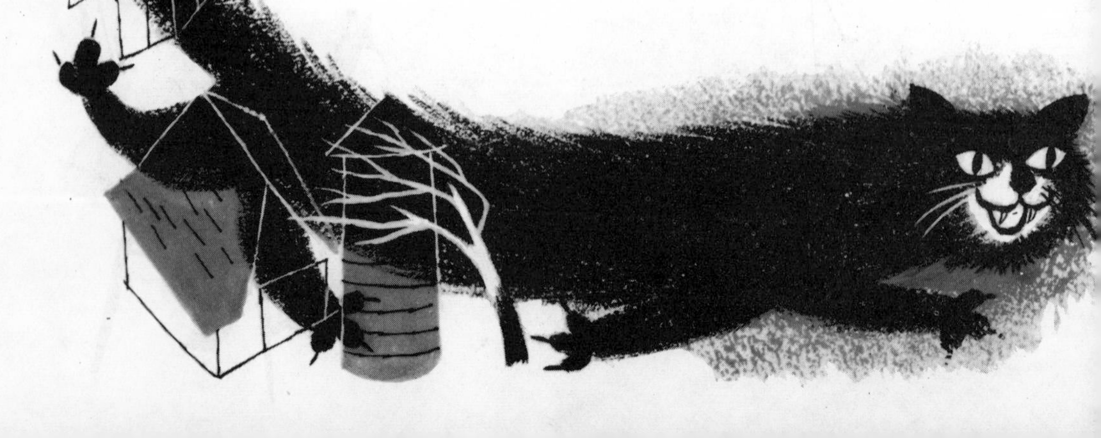

The Wind

The wind has such a rainy sound
   Moaning through the town,
The sea has such a windy sound,—
   Will the ships go down?

The apples in the orchard
   Tumble from their tree.—
Oh, will the ships go down, go down,
   In the windy sea?

—Christina Georgina Rossetti

The Isle Should Have a Pine Tree

It takes a little island
To button down a pond
Within its frill of shores and woods
And pleated hills beyond.

The isle should have a pine tree,
The tree should have a bird,
And the bird should sing the sweetest
   song
The ear has ever heard.

—Elizabeth Coatsworth

Holding Hands

Elephants walking
Along the trails

Are holding hands
By holding tails.

Trunks and tails
Are handy things

When elephants walk
In Circus rings.

Elephants work
And elephants play

And elephants walk
And feel so gay.

And when they walk—
It never fails

They're holding hands
By holding tails.

—*Lenore M. Link*

The Circus

Friday came and the circus was there,
And Mother said that the twins and I
And Charles and Clarence and all of us
Could go out and see the parade go by.

And there were wagons with pictures on,
And you never could guess what they had inside,
Nobody could guess, for the doors were shut,
And there was a dog that a monkey
  could ride.

A man on the top of a sort of cart
Was clapping his hands and making a talk.
And the elephant came—he can step pretty far—
It made us laugh to see him walk.

Three beautiful ladies came riding by,
And each one had on a golden dress,
And each one had a golden whip.
They were queens of Sheba, I guess.

A big wild man was in a cage,
And he had some snakes going over his feet.
And somebody said, "He eats them alive!"
But I didn't see him eat.

            —*Elizabeth Madox Roberts*

Moon Song

There is a star that runs very fast,
That goes pulling the moon
Through the tops of the poplars.
It is all in silver,
The tall star:
The moon rolls goldenly along
Out of breath.
Mr. Moon, does he make you hurry?
                    —*Hilda Conkling*

The White Window

The Moon comes every night to peep
Through the window where I lie;
But I pretend to be asleep;
And watch the Moon go slowly by,—
And she never makes a sound!

She stands and stares! And then she goes
To the house that's next to me,
Stealing by on tippy-toes;
To peep at folk asleep maybe—
And she never makes a sound!

                    —*James Stephens*

"Moon Song" reprinted by permission of the publishers, J. B. Lippincott Company, from POEMS BY A LITTLE GIRL by Hilda Conkling. Copyright, 1920, 1948, by J. B. Lippincott Company.

The Falling Star

I saw a star slide down the sky,
Blinding the north as it went by,
Too burning and too quick to hold,
Too lovely to be bought or sold,
Good only to make wishes on
And then forever to be gone.

—*Sara Teasdale*

Daisies

At evening when I go to bed
I see the stars shine overhead;
They are the little daisies white
That dot the meadow of the Night.

And often while I'm dreaming so,
Across the sky the Moon will go;
It is a lady, sweet and fair,
Who comes to gather daisies there.

For, when at morning I arise,
There's not a star left in the skies;
She's picked them all and
    dropped them down
Into the meadows of the town.

—*Frank Dempster Sherman*

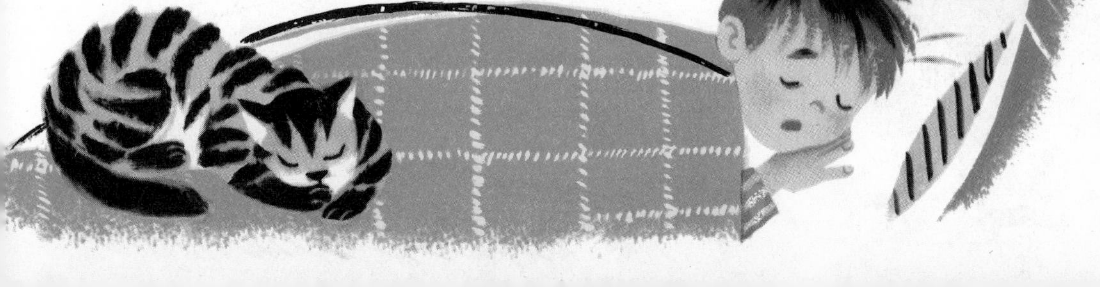

From a Railway Carriage

Faster than fairies, faster than witches,
Bridges and houses, hedges and ditches;
And charging along like troops in a battle,
All through the meadows the horses and
cattle:

All of the sights of the hill and the plain
Fly as thick as driving rain;
And ever again, in the wink of an eye,
Painted stations whistle by.

Here is a child who clambers and scrambles
All by himself and gathering brambles;
Here is a tramp who stands and gazes;
And there is the green for stringing
the daisies!

Here is a cart run away in the road
Lumping along with man and load;
And here is a mill, and there is a river:
Each a glimpse and gone forever!

—*Robert Louis Stevenson*

Moving

I like to move. There's such a feeling
  Of hurrying
    and scurrying,
And such a feeling
Of men with trunks and packing cases,
Of kitchen clocks and mother's laces,
Dusters, dishes, books and vases,
Toys and pans and candles.

I always find things I'd forgotten,
An old brown Teddy stuffed with cotton,
Some croquet mallets without handles,
A marble and my worn-out sandals,
A half an engine and a hat . . .
And I like that.

I like to watch the big vans backing,
And the lumbering
  and the cumbering,
And the hammering and the tacking.
I even like the packing!

And that will prove
I like to move!

—*Eunice Tietjens*

Yet Gentle Will the Griffin Be

The moon? It is a griffin's egg,
Hatching tomorrow night.
And how the little boys will watch
With shouting and delight
To see him break the shell and stretch
And creep across the sky.
The boys will laugh. The little girls,
I fear, may hide and cry.
Yet gentle will the griffin be,
Most decorous and fat,
And walk up to the Milky Way
And lap it like a cat.

—*Vachel Lindsay*

Strong Magic

Dragons breathing smoke and flames,
Little men with funny names,
Princesses with hearts of ice,
Elves and leprechauns for spice—
The world was younger and more gay
When magic happened every day.

—*Dorothy Hall*

The Enchanted Rabbit

Robin Palmer

All the rabbits at the meeting looked very solemn. Hops, a small brown rabbit, sat beside his mother trying to understand.

Old Man Tickleson, the meanest farmer in six counties, was after the rabbits again. He shot at them. He set traps. Lately he had been throwing out poisoned lettuce leaves. And yet the rabbits had never even nibbled one pea in Farmer Tickleson's garden, so tight was the fence. The rabbits' meeting was to see what in the world could be done.

"I can think of only one answer to our problem," the oldest rabbit said. "We must hunt tirelessly for a four-leaf clover."

"Why?" whispered Hops to his mother.

"A rabbit who finds a four-leaf clover has magic power," his mother said.

"But I found one yesterday," said Hops.

Mrs. Rabbit threw up her paws in surprise. "What did you do with it?" she asked.

"I ate it."

"Order!" shouted the oldest rabbit.

"Hops has eaten a four-leaf clover," explained his mother.

Immediately, all the other rabbits stared at Hops in wonder and admiration. "Are you sure? Did you count carefully?" they asked.

"Order," the oldest rabbit shouted again. "Tomorrow six of us will go to Old Man Tickleson's. Hops will say, 'Pouf, I'm a dragon.' If he has eaten a four-leaf clover, he will become one."

Hops shook with excitement. "But suppose I don't enjoy being a dragon."

"The change," said the oldest rabbit, "is not lasting. In four hours, you will begin to shrink. Now I will teach you what to do and say."

Next morning Hops left the five other rabbits in the bushes by the farmer's house. He stepped out on the lawn. "Pouf," he said, "I'm a dragon."

Instantly strange things began to happen. Hops felt like a balloon that is being blown up, but it didn't hurt. When he stopped growing, he turned his head to admire himself. He had a long tail covered with metallic green scales. His body was covered with scales, too. Of course, he couldn't see his face, but he was sure it must be fierce. When he breathed, smoke came out of his mouth.

Hops was so pleased that for a moment he forgot all about the farmer. Then he heard a whistling sound and a bullet flew past his ear. A second bullet struck the hard scales on his side and bounced off.

"Ah-ha, he can't hurt me," thought the bunny-dragon. Looking about, he saw the farmer in an upstairs window. Then Hops called out (for of course all dragons can speak perfect English), "Come outside and fight in the open, Mr. Tickle-son."

Now the farmer had been upset at seeing a dragon on his front lawn. When the dragon called him by name, he was more alarmed than ever. It made the visit so personal.

"Have you nothing to say for yourself?" asked Hops.

The farmer tried once more to aim his gun, but his fingers were stiff with fear. He called out in a weak voice, "Go away."

Hops laughed. The wonderful metallic sound of his laughter thrilled him. To Mr. Tickleson it was terrifying.

"What shall I do?" he thought. He lived all

alone. His farm was a long way from the village. Then he remembered the police. It was their business to handle things like this. He went to the telephone. "Police," he said hoarsely. "Get me the police station."

The operator connected him quickly.

"Tickleson, J. P. Tickleson speaking. Come out here. Hurry!"

"Now, now, Mr. Tickleson," said the police chief, who was in the middle of a good jigsaw puzzle. "Calm down and tell me what's wrong."

"Dragons!" shouted the farmer.

"Ah," said the policeman. "Where?"

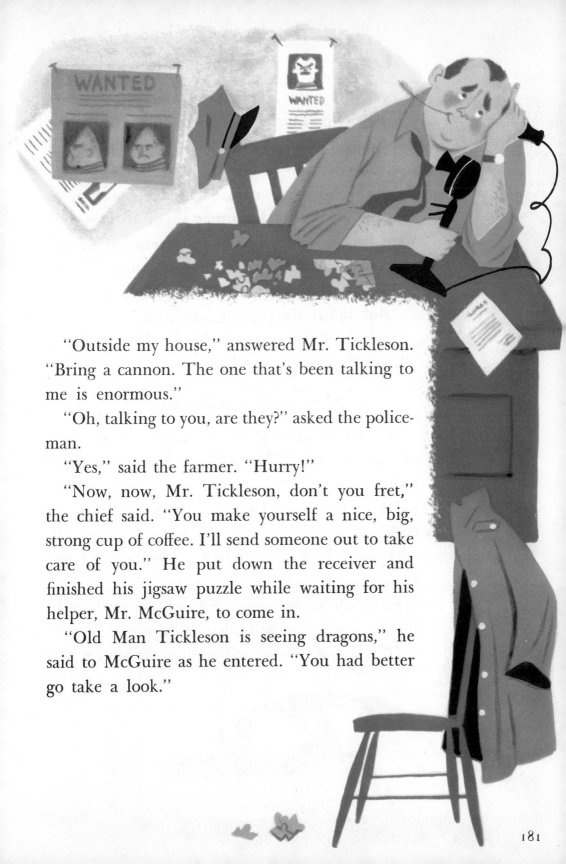

"Outside my house," answered Mr. Tickleson. "Bring a cannon. The one that's been talking to me is enormous."

"Oh, talking to you, are they?" asked the policeman.

"Yes," said the farmer. "Hurry!"

"Now, now, Mr. Tickleson, don't you fret," the chief said. "You make yourself a nice, big, strong cup of coffee. I'll send someone out to take care of you." He put down the receiver and finished his jigsaw puzzle while waiting for his helper, Mr. McGuire, to come in.

"Old Man Tickleson is seeing dragons," he said to McGuire as he entered. "You had better go take a look."

McGuire took a fireman along, in case he needed help. The two of them drove out to the Tickleson house. As they came to the gate, the fireman cried out, "Hold on. Look at *that!*"

Mr. McGuire was a brave man. He looked twice to make sure. Then he turned his car around and went back to town as fast as he could go. It was hard to make the chief believe his story.

"You and Tickleson are *both* crazy," he said.

"But Smith, the fireman, saw it, too."

The chief scratched his head. "I must think what to do," he muttered.

How To Cope With Dragons

In the meantime Hops was trying to talk with the farmer. But Mr. Tickleson was too excited to listen. He ran from window to window, watching for the police. He saw McGuire's car turn back.

"Idiots," he said to himself. "They might have known they'd need more than two men."

He sat down and rested his head on his hands. It was then he noticed what Hops was saying.

"If you won't do what I ask, I shall blow some

sparks into your hayloft and burn your barn down. I might even burn your house, too." And Hops blew out a warning puff of smoke.

"Stop it, stop it," screamed the farmer. "Spare me! I've never done you any harm."

"Yes, you have," cried Hops. "Every time you hunt a rabbit, it is a personal insult to me. I am the champion of the rabbits. All I ask of you is a written treaty that you will never harm them again. If you make this treaty and keep it, I shan't hurt you."

The farmer grunted. "Why didn't you say so in the first place?" he asked.

"I *have* been saying it over and over," cried Hops. "Now get a pen and paper and come out here."

"Never!" shouted Mr. Tickleson. He instantly disappeared in a cloud of smoke. "Why can't I do it here?" he said.

"Because the witnesses prefer you to come out," Hops answered coldly. "Will you come out at once? Or is it time for some sparks?"

"Oh, I'll come, I'll come," said the farmer quickly. He got his writing things and went outside. There he was embarrassed to find that the witnesses were all rabbits.

Hops dictated the treaty. He ordered Mr. Tickleson to make two copies and sign both of them. One was to be kept by the rabbits.

"I hope," said the dragon, "that I shall never have to punish you for breaking this promise."

"You won't," said the farmer earnestly.

"Very good," Hops replied. Then he amused himself by going off to the village and looking into the police station. He scared the chief so badly that he never touched a jigsaw puzzle again. He said puzzles reminded him of dragons.

But Hops was glad to become a rabbit once more. As for Mr. Tickleson, he never hurt any animal from that time on. And he always had a funny feeling that wherever he went, whatever he did, rabbits were somewhere watching him.

The Lad Who Went to the North Wind

A Scandinavian Folk Tale

Once upon a time there was a widow who had one son. She was sick and she was feeble, and the son had to help around the house.

"Son," she said one day, "go out to the storehouse and get some meal for our porridge."

So the lad went out to the storehouse for the meal. Just as he was coming down the steps with the ground meal in his hands—"Pfff!" came the North Wind and scattered it all about.

The boy went back for more meal. Again the North Wind blew it out of his hands. The same thing happened a third time.

Then the boy decided this must stop. "Poor folk like us can't afford to lose good food. I'll just look up the North Wind at his home and ask him to give the meal back."

So the widow's son set out for the home of the North Wind. He walked and he walked and he walked. And after a long while he came to the place where the North Wind lived.

"Good day," said the lad to the North Wind. "And thank you for coming to see us yesterday." He had decided to be polite.

"GOOD DAY," said the North Wind. He tried to be polite, too, but he roared as he spoke. He couldn't help it. "THANK YOU FOR COMING TO SEE ME. YOU HAVE SOMETHING ON YOUR MIND, I SUPPOSE?"

"Yes," said the lad boldly. "Please be so kind as to give me back the meal you blew out of my hands on the storehouse steps yesterday. My mother is sick and she is feeble, and without our bit of meal we shall starve."

"I'm sorry," roared the wind. "I don't have your meal, but I'll give you something in its place. Just shake out this cloth. Say, 'Cloth, spread yourself!' and it will give you all kinds of food."

Well, that sounded good to the boy. He took the cloth and set off for home, well content.

But he had come so far he couldn't get back home all in one day. So he stopped for the night at an inn. Not having enough money to buy food, he shook out the cloth on a corner of the inn table, and said, "Cloth, spread yourself!" Instantly all sorts of good things were before him, and he sat down and ate with a will.

The landlord stood by, bug-eyed, to see this marvelous cloth. "I'm a fool," he thought to himself, "if I can't get that cloth away from this stupid boy." So waiting until the lad was asleep, he took the cloth, and put another one in its place.

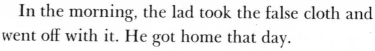

In the morning, the lad took the false cloth and went off with it. He got home that day.

"Now, Mother, I've been off to see the North Wind," said he. "North Wind said he was sorry for taking our meal, and just see what he gave me."

So the lad took out his cloth and shook it and said, "Cloth, spread yourself!" But alas, the cloth couldn't spread so much as a piece of dry bread.

"Well," said the boy, "that's a pretty trick. Now I'll just have to go back to the North Wind again." And off he went.

"Good evening!" said the lad.

"Good evening!" roared the North Wind.

"About that cloth you gave me for the meal you spilled—it won't spread up so much as a piece of dry bread. I want my meal back," said the boy.

"I don't have your meal," roared the wind. "But yonder is a ram that drops gold pieces out of its mouth. All you have to say is 'Ram, ram, make money!' Will you take that for your meal?"

The boy tried out the ram, which sure enough dropped a gold coin for him. So he said he would take the beast, and started off home with it.

But again he stopped for the night at the same

inn. The rascal of a landlord wormed out of the boy what the ram could do. So in the middle of the night, when the boy was asleep, he took the ram and put an ordinary one in its place.

So the boy went off home with the false ram. "Mother, the North Wind is a very fine fellow, after all," said he. "Look at this ram, now. All I need to say is, 'Ram, ram, make money!' and we'll have all the gold coins we can use."

But the ram didn't make any money. He just stood there, looking like a stupid sheep.

"I *will* have my money's worth for that meal," said the boy. So back he went to the North Wind, and told him in no uncertain terms that the ram was no good. What *was* the wind going to do about that meal?

"Well," roared the North Wind, "I've nothing else to give you but that old stick in the corner. If you say, 'Stick, stick, lay on!' it will go on beating until you say, 'Stick, stick, now stop!'"

That gave the boy an idea. He took the stick and went along back, as usual, till he came to the inn. And pretty soon he lay down on the bench and pretended to be asleep.

The landlord thought for sure that the stick must be valuable, too. So at midnight he came softly into the room with another stick, to change the two. But the lad had been waiting for that, and he yelled with all his might, "Stick, stick, lay on!"

Oh, what a to-do that was! The landlord jumped over tables and benches. He knocked against shelves and set the dishes rolling. He bumped into doors. He bawled and roared for mercy. But he could not get away from the stick. At last he yelled, "Stop it and I'll give you back your tablecloth and ram."

So the lad said, "Stick, stick, now stop!" And he got his tablecloth and his ram and went out of there, with the stick in his hand. And you may believe his mother was glad to see him come again, and she soon got well, and they lived merrily from that time on.

Snow-White and Rose-Red

Retold from the Brothers Grimm

There was once a poor widow who lived in a little cottage at the edge of a forest. In front of the cottage bloomed two rose-trees, one with red flowers and one with white. The widow had two daughters, so pretty and sweet that she named them after the rose-trees, Rose-Red and Snow-White.

Snow-White was quiet and gentle in all her ways. Rose-Red was merrier. She was likely to be off chasing butterflies while Snow-White was helping her mother in the house.

But the two girls loved their mother and loved each other dearly. And they were so kind and good that no animal in all the forest would harm them.

One cold winter evening, while the kettle sang on the hearth and the mother was reading a story to the girls, there came a knock at the door.

"Open the door, Rose-Red!" the mother cried. "Perhaps, this bitter night, some traveler has lost his way."

So Rose-Red unbarred the door. But there, instead of a poor traveler, stood a great black bear! Rose-Red was frightened. She would have shut the door again, but the bear called out to her in a man's voice.

"Do not be afraid," said the bear. "I will do you no harm. But I am half-frozen, and beg that I may warm myself at your fire."

"Poor bear!" said the mother. "Come lie beside the hearth. Only take care not to get a spark on your shaggy coat."

"My fur is full of snow," said the bear. "Perhaps your daughters would bring brooms and sweep it off before I come in."

So Snow-White and Rose-Red got their brooms and swept the bear. Then he lay down before the fire. In a little while the girls forgot completely to be afraid of him. He was such a gentle, kind bear! They romped with him and pulled his fur and played so many tricks that more than once he called out:

> *Children dear, leave me my life,*
> *Or else you'll never be called wife.*

When bedtime came, the mother said, "You may stay here and sleep, if you like." So the bear slept before the hearth, and the children let him out in the morning. Every evening after that, all winter long, the bear came trotting to the cottage, and the door was never barred until he came.

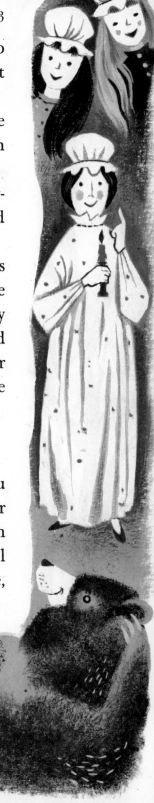

But, with the spring, the woods turned green. The birds began to return. One morning, when Snow-White came to let the bear out, he seemed quite sad.

"Dear Snow-White," he said, sighing, "I must say goodbye for a while."

"Alas, dear bear," said Snow-White, "where are you going?"

"I must stay in the forest to guard my treasures," he answered. "In the winter the evil dwarfs are kept in their holes by the snow and the ice. But in the summer the dwarfs go everywhere, and they are great thieves."

So Snow-White opened the door for her friend. But she opened it slowly and sadly. As the bear pushed through, he tore his shaggy coat. Snow-

White was not sure, but for a moment she thought she saw a golden gleam under the fur.

Some time afterwards, Rose-Red and Snow-White went into the forest to gather sticks for the fire.

"What is that," Rose-Red asked, "bobbing up and down on the log?"

The girls went near to see. There was a dwarf with a snowy white beard a yard long! His beard was caught in a crack in the log, and the little man was hopping around trying to pull himself free.

He glared at the girls with his little red eyes. "Don't just stand there, you great, stupid girls!" he snapped. "Help me get loose."

"How did you happen to get caught here?" Rose-Red asked, as she helped to pull.

"Of all the foolish questions!" panted the dwarf. "An idiot could see that as I was splitting this log for firewood, the wedge slipped and the log closed up again."

But no matter how they pulled, the children could not get the little man's beard free.

"Well," said Snow-White, "there is only one

thing to do." And taking her scissors out of her pocket, she cut off the end of the dwarf's beard.

The Ungrateful Dwarf

The little fellow was not a bit grateful. "Plague take you!" he screamed. "You have spoiled my beautiful beard. May bad luck follow you!" And he jumped up, seized a sack of gold which lay hidden in the roots of a tree, and marched off.

A few days later Snow-White and Rose-Red went fishing. As they drew near the pond, they heard a shrill little voice and saw something jumping up and down. It was the dwarf again.

"Help me, you!" he screamed when he saw them. "This brute of a fish is pulling me into the water!"

And so it was. Somehow the dwarf's beard and the fishing line had got tangled up together, just

as a large fish came along. The girls were soon able to rescue the little man from the fish. But getting the fishing line untangled from his beard was a harder matter. Again, Snow-White slipped out her scissors. She cut two more little pieces off his beard.

"Donkey!" screamed the little man. "May the crows peck you for ruining my beautiful beard!" He took up a bag of pearls which lay nearby in the rushes, and slipped away.

Not very many days later the girls were on their way to town, to buy needles and thread and ribbon for their mother. Their road lay across an open place strewn with large rocks. Above the rocks a bird was circling. As they watched it, they saw it dive and heard a scream. Running up, they found that the bird had seized their old acquaintance the dwarf, and was trying to carry him off.

The girls laid hold of the dwarf and soon frightened the bird away. They were used to the little man, and were not surprised when he said, "Great, clumsy things! Why did you have to tear my coat?" And picking up a bag of precious stones, he disappeared.

On their way back from town, the girls passed the same place. There they came upon the dwarf again. He had emptied his bag of stones onto a large, flat rock, and was letting them slip through his fingers. With the sun shining through them, the stones were so beautiful that the girls stopped to admire.

The dwarf saw them watching him. He jumped up in a fury. "So you want to steal my stones!" he yelled. "Get away, or I will do you an injury." And he picked up a large stone to throw at them.

Just at this moment a big black bear rushed out of the forest near by. The dwarf saw him and tried to run, but he was not fast enough.

"Spare me, dear bear!" begged the dwarf. "Eat up those stupid girls instead. They'll make a much better meal than poor little me."

The bear only growled and gave the dwarf one

blow with his big paw. And that was the end of the dwarf.

Rose-Red and Snow-White were running away in fright, when a voice they knew called after them. "Do not run, children. It is I."

And there was their own friend the bear. As he came up to them, suddenly his rough coat fell off. A handsome young man dressed in gold stood there!

"I am a king's son," he said. "This wicked dwarf stole all my treasures, and turned me into a bear. Only his death would set me free. But until today I could never catch him."

So they all went home rejoicing. In time, Snow-White married the prince and Rose-Red married his brother. And they took their mother to the palace to live with them. In front of the palace, for years and years, the red and white rose-trees bloomed all summer long.

The Sorcerer's Apprentice

Old Folk Tale

Once there was a sorcerer, a great magician. His spells and magic were in such demand that he had an apprentice to help him. This apprentice was a well-meaning lad, but a somewhat foolish one. Working with a magician had gone to his head. He thought he knew more than he did.

One day, the sorcerer set off on a journey. He left the boy plenty of work, with strict orders to get all of it finished.

The boy watched until his master was out of sight. Then he flung up his cap and did a jig. "Hurray!" he cried. "Why waste my time on these dull tasks? I'll make some magic—like the master himself! Now what shall I do first?"

Looking about, the boy spied the broom, leaning against the wall. "Ah!" cried the boy. "I shall bring the broom to life!" Only yesterday he had heard the spell the master used for such things.

The boy spoke the words. Slowly the broom stood upright. Stiffly and solemnly it advanced toward him. He knew that he must set it a task.

"Bring water from the well!" Proud and a little scared, the boy watched the broom bring a bucket of water from the well—and then another bucket.

"Enough," said the boy, waving his hand.

But the broom did not stop. Stiffly, solemnly, it brought another bucket of water from the well— and then another—and then another. By this time, water was running over the floor.

"Stop! Stop!" But still the broom went on bringing water. It was working faster now. And suddenly, the boy realized why he could not stop it. He did not know the words to break the spell! Seizing the ax, he chopped the broom in two.

That was a terrible mistake. Instantly, both halves of the broom began to bring water, each twice as fast as before! The fire went out. Tables and chairs began to float. The boy, too frightened to move, was sure that he would drown.

At last, the sorcerer returned. He saw water pouring from his front door and hurried faster. When he understood what had happened, he spoke the word of power. The broom fell down lifeless; the water flowed away. And the boy threw himself at his master's feet, content at last to be only the sorcerer's apprentice.

Tonino and the Fairies

Ralph Steele Boggs and Mary Gould Davis

Tonino the Hunchback was the merriest fellow in all the city of Granada. In spite of the hump on his back and the pain that came when the cold winds swept down from the Sierra Nevada Mountains, he was always ready with a smile.

He always had a bit of fun to poke at the housewives when he stopped before their door with his herd of goats. From the old grandmother to the latest baby, the family would gather around Tonino. They would listen delightedly to his sayings, while he milked the goats. The men of Granada liked Tonino, too.

No gathering at the Inn was complete without Tonino. He could sing like a bird, and he knew all the old songs of Spain—ballads and folk songs and the marching tunes of the soldiers. The ballads he sang with such fire that even the roughest of his hearers listened spellbound. The songs he sang with such a rhythm that heads were set to wagging and feet to dancing.

From THREE GOLDEN ORANGES by Ralph Steele Boggs and Mary Gould Davis, copyright 1936. Reprinted by permission of the publishers, Longmans, Green and Co., Inc.

And, when the merrymaking was over, Tonino
was always given his share of the good things to
eat and drink. Often he tucked a handful of cakes
and an orange or some dried figs and nuts into
his pocket to take to old Tia Teresa. She lived
with Tonino in the cave hollowed out of the hillside. Between the milk of his goats and his gift
of song, Tonino and Tia Teresa fared well. And
no matter how much his crooked back hurt him,
neither Tia Teresa nor anyone else ever heard
Tonino complain.

One night, when the gathering in the Inn had
lasted later than usual, Tonino tucked his guitar
under his arm and started toward home. It was
St. John's Eve, and the June moon hung low in
the sky. The high peaks of the Sierra Nevada stood
cold and white under it. Even in midsummer,
the snow clothed them.

Tonino walked on slowly, the tunes that he had played still singing themselves in his head. On the side of the hill there stood an olive tree, old and gnarled, its leaves silvery white in the moonlight. Just above it, Tonino sat down on the short, dry grass. He took off his cap and let the cool night wind blow through his hair. It had been a long, hot day and a long evening. Tonino was tired. He rested his head on one outflung arm and slept.

When he awoke, the moon had set. The stars blazed low and bright in the sky. Through the stillness, there came to Tonino a faint thread of song. At first it was only music. Then, thin and clear, he heard the words:

> *Monday and Tuesday and Wednesday*
>   *make three,*
> *Monday and Tuesday and Wednesday*
>   *make three.*

Now Tonino knew the air—old and wild. He raised himself on his elbow. Down below him, under the olive tree, the fairies were dancing. There were hundreds of them, tiny fairy men and fairy women. With heads lifted and hands joined,

they were dancing in a circle around the old tree. Their impish faces shone white in the starlight.

They were so intent on their dance, so lost in their song, that they did not even see Tonino. He stared at them in delight and wonder. Often he had heard of the fairies, but never had he seen them.

> *Monday and Tuesday and Wednesday
>   make three,
> Monday and Tuesday and Wednesday
>   make three—*

round and round and round the tree, until Tonino grew dizzy with it!

"Hold, my little masters. If you do not know the rest of the song, I will give you a hint of it."

Lifting his guitar, he swept his fingers over the strings. He sang in his clear voice:

> *Monday and Tuesday and Wednesday*
> *   make three,*
> *Thursday and Friday and Saturday,*
> *   six!*

The fairies shouted with joy. Instantly their tiny voices took up the words. They sang with Tonino until the valley rang with the song.

> *Monday and Tuesday and Wednesday*
> *   make three,*
> *Thursday and Friday and Saturday,*
> *   six!—*

higher and shriller and sweeter until the very stars seemed to sing with them.

Suddenly the song ceased. The circle was broken. The fairies, one and all, ran up the hill to Tonino. They swarmed all over him. They clung to his fingers with their tiny hands, looking at him with mischievous, slanting eyes.

"A reward, Tonino! A reward!" they cried. "Make a wish and we will grant it!"

Tonino chuckled. "I want no reward, little masters," he answered. "It is enough to have seen you and to have sung with you."

But the fairies insisted. "Make a wish," they shouted. "Any wish. And we will grant it."

Tonino thought for a moment. "There is this hump of mine," he said. "It is heavy to carry. It aches when the weather is cold. Could you take it away from me?"

Instantly a thousand little hands were laid on his shoulders. His body felt lifted and lightened. A white mist rose from the valley. Through it, ever fainter and sweeter, came the fairy voices:

Monday and Tuesday and Wednesday
make three,
Thursday and Friday and Saturday,
six!

Tonino rose to his feet, as straight and strong in body as he was in spirit.

There was much excitement in Granada when Tonino's tale was told. Nothing else was talked about for days. No one grudged him his good fortune. And everywhere he went, the eyes of the pretty girls of Granada followed him.

The Fairies

Up the airy mountain,
   Down the rushy glen,
We daren't go a-hunting
   For fear of little men;
Wee folk, good folk,
   Trooping all together;
Green jacket, red cap,
   And white owl's feather!

Down along the rocky shore
   Some make their home,
They live on crispy pancakes
   Of yellow tide-foam;
Some in the reeds
   Of the black mountain-lake
With frogs for their watch-dogs,
   All night awake.

By the craggy hill-side,
   Through the mosses bare,
They have planted thorn-trees
   For pleasure here and there.
Is any man so daring
   As to dig one up in spite,
He shall find the thornies set
   In his bed at night.

Up the airy mountain,
   Down the rushy glen,
We daren't go a-hunting
   For fear of little men;
Wee folk, good folk,
   Trooping all together;
Green jacket, red cap,
   And white owl's feather!
       —*William Allingham*

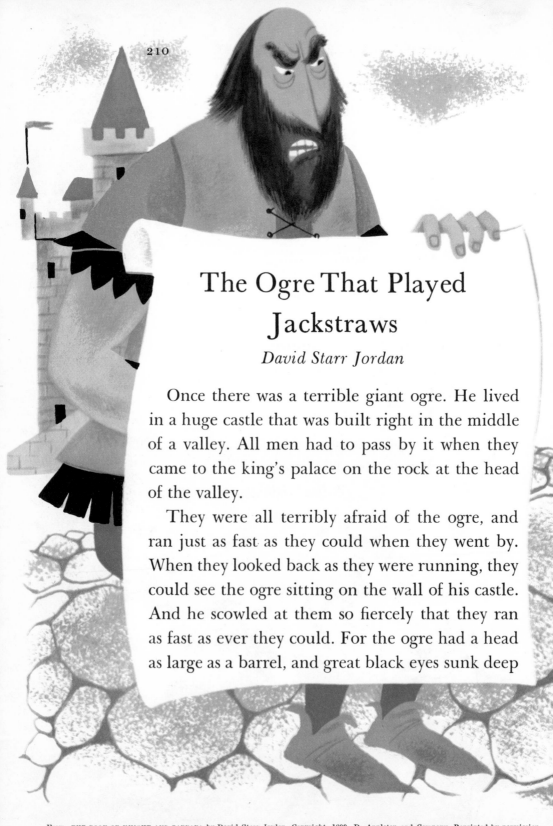

The Ogre That Played Jackstraws

David Starr Jordan

Once there was a terrible giant ogre. He lived in a huge castle that was built right in the middle of a valley. All men had to pass by it when they came to the king's palace on the rock at the head of the valley.

They were all terribly afraid of the ogre, and ran just as fast as they could when they went by. When they looked back as they were running, they could see the ogre sitting on the wall of his castle. And he scowled at them so fiercely that they ran as fast as ever they could. For the ogre had a head as large as a barrel, and great black eyes sunk deep under long bushy eyelashes. And when he opened his mouth, they saw it was full of teeth. So they ran away faster than ever, without caring to see any more.

The king wanted to get rid of the ogre, and he sent his men to drive the ogre away and to tear down his castle. But the ogre scowled at them so savagely that their teeth began to fall out. They all turned back and said they dare not fight such a horrid creature.

Roger, the king's son, rode his black horse Hurricane up against the door of the ogre's castle, and struck hard against it with his iron glove. Then the door opened and the ogre came out. He seized Roger in one hand and the great black horse in the other and rubbed their heads together. While he did this he made them very small. Then he tumbled them over the wall into the ogre's garden. And they crawled through a hole in the garden fence and both ran home, Roger one way and Hurricane the other. Neither dared tell the king or anyone else where he had been, nor what the ogre had done to him. But it was two or three days before they became large again.

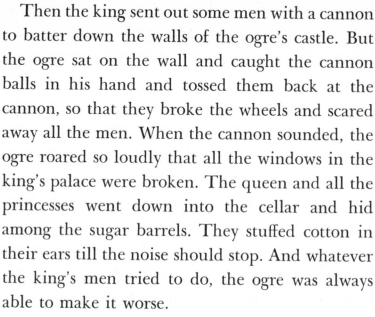

Then the king sent out some men with a cannon to batter down the walls of the ogre's castle. But the ogre sat on the wall and caught the cannon balls in his hand and tossed them back at the cannon, so that they broke the wheels and scared away all the men. When the cannon sounded, the ogre roared so loudly that all the windows in the king's palace were broken. The queen and all the princesses went down into the cellar and hid among the sugar barrels. They stuffed cotton in their ears till the noise should stop. And whatever the king's men tried to do, the ogre was always able to make it worse.

At last no one dared to go out into the valley beside the ogre's castle. No one dared look at it from anywhere. When the ogre scowled, all who saw him dropped to the ground with fear, and their teeth began to fall out. And when the ogre roared there was no one who could bear to hear it.

So the king and all his men hid in the cellar of the castle with the queen and the princesses. They stuffed their ears full of cotton, and the ogre scowled and roared and had his own way.

But there was one little boy named Pennyroyal,

who tended the black horse Hurricane. He was not afraid of anything, because he was a little boy. The little boy said he would go out and see the ogre and tell him to go away. And they were all so scared that they could not ask him not to go.

So Pennyroyal put on his hat, filled his pockets with marbles and took his kite under his arm, and went down the valley to the castle of the ogre. The ogre sat on the wall and looked at him. But the little boy was not afraid. It did the ogre no good to scowl. Then Pennyroyal knocked on the ogre's door, and the ogre opened it and looked at the little boy.

"Please, Mr. Ogre, may I come in?" said Pennyroyal. The ogre opened the door, and the little boy began to walk around the castle looking at all the things.

There was one room filled with bones, but the ogre was ashamed of it, and did not want to let the little boy see it. So when Pennyroyal was not looking, the ogre just changed the room and made it small. Instead of a room full of bones it became just a box of jackstraws.

And the big elephant he had there to play with

he made into a lap-elephant, and the little boy took it in his hand and stroked its tiny tusks and tied a knot in its trunk. Everything that could frighten the little boy the ogre made small and pretty, so that they had great times together.

By and by the ogre grew smaller and smaller. He took off his ugly old face with the long teeth and bushy eyebrows and dropped them on the floor and covered them with a wolf-skin. The little boy sat down on the floor beside him, and they began to play jackstraws with the box of jackstraws that had been a room full of bones. The ogre had never been a boy himself, so jackstraws was the only game he knew how to play.

The elephant he had made small snuggled down between them on the floor. And as they played with each other, the castle itself grew small, and shrank away until there was just room enough for them and their game.

Up in the palace, when the ogre stopped roaring, the king's men looked out and saw that the ogre's castle was gone. Then Roger, the king's son, called for Pennyroyal. But when he could not find the boy, he saddled the black horse Hurricane himself and rode down the valley to where the ogre's castle had been. When he came back he told the king that the ogre and his castle were all gone.

Where the castle stood there was nothing left but a board tent under the oak tree. In the tent there were just two little boys playing jackstraws. Between them on the ground lay a candy elephant.

That was all. For the terrible ogre was one of that kind of ogres that will do to folks what folks do to them. There isn't any other kind of ogre.

Rumpelstiltskin

Retold from the Brothers Grimm

Once upon a time there was a miller with a pretty daughter. One day, having some business with the King, the miller wanted to seem important. So he said to the King, "Your Majesty, my daughter is so clever that she can spin straw into gold!"

The miller was only foolish. But the King was greedy, which is worse.

"That is a skill worth having," said the King. "If your daughter is as clever as you say, bring her here tomorrow without fail."

What was the poor man to do? Of course he brought her, and left her at the palace, hoping for the best. The King led the girl into a room

216

piled full of straw. The only other furnishings were a spinning wheel, some bobbins, and a stool.

"Now, my pretty maid," the King said, "your father tells me you can spin straw into gold. If you haven't spun all this straw into gold by sunrise tomorrow morning, you shall die."

Then the King went out and shut the door and locked it. The poor girl sank down on the stool in despair. Spin straw into gold? Who ever heard of such a thing? She began to cry.

Suddenly the door opened. In whisked a queer little man with a long gray beard.

"Why are you crying, pretty maid?" he asked.

"Oh," said the poor girl, "my father told the King I could spin straw into gold. So now I must spin all this straw into gold by tomorrow morning, or else lose my life."

"What will you give me if I spin it for you?" asked the little man.

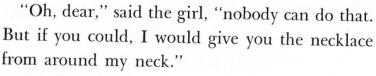

"Oh, dear," said the girl, "nobody can do that. But if you could, I would give you the necklace from around my neck."

"Well, I can do it, so give me the necklace."

The girl gave him the necklace, and the little man sat down at the spinning wheel. Whir, whir, whir, the wheel went round three times, and the bobbin was full of gold! Then he put on another bobbin. Whir, whir, whir, the wheel went round three times and the second bobbin was full of gold. The miller's daughter was crying with joy now. She was so glad that she did not have to die.

The little man spun all night. By morning, the straw was shining gold.

Promptly at sunrise came the King. He was delighted to find so much gold, but was still greedy. Later that day he led the miller's daughter into a much larger room filled with straw.

"This straw, too, must be gold by tomorrow morning," said the King. "Else you shall die."

Again the poor frightened girl sat down and wept. Again the queer little man appeared.

"And what will you give me this time, if I spin the straw into gold for you?"

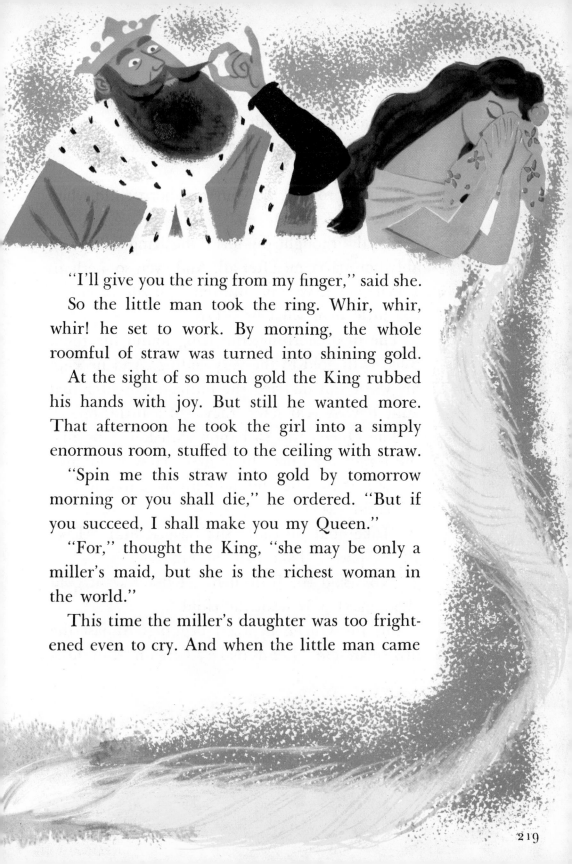

"I'll give you the ring from my finger," said she.

So the little man took the ring. Whir, whir, whir! he set to work. By morning, the whole roomful of straw was turned into shining gold.

At the sight of so much gold the King rubbed his hands with joy. But still he wanted more. That afternoon he took the girl into a simply enormous room, stuffed to the ceiling with straw.

"Spin me this straw into gold by tomorrow morning or you shall die," he ordered. "But if you succeed, I shall make you my Queen."

"For," thought the King, "she may be only a miller's maid, but she is the richest woman in the world."

This time the miller's daughter was too frightened even to cry. And when the little man came and asked her what she would give him, she could only stare at him with wide eyes.

"Nothing," she said at last. "I have nothing left to give."

"Then promise me your first-born child when you become the Queen."

"Well," thought the girl, "the King will probably not marry me after all. And even so, perhaps I shall not have any children." So she promised the little man what he asked.

The next morning, the King found the room piled with gold to the very ceiling. And he kept his word and married the miller's daughter that same day. A year later, they had a little son.

The Queen was so happy with her baby that she forgot the queer little man. How frightened she was, then, when he suddenly appeared to take the child away!

"Take gold instead!" she begged him. "Take all my jewels. Take half the kingdom."

"No," said the little man. "I don't want gold or jewels. I only want the child."

But the Queen kept on begging. At last the little man said, "Let us make a bargain. If in three

days you can guess my name, you may keep your baby."

So the Queen spent the entire night thinking of all the names she knew. She sent a trusted messenger through the country to collect any new names he could find. And the next day, when the little man came, the Queen had a great long list.

She began with Caspar, Melchior, and Balthazar. She called all the names she knew. But at each one the little man said, "That's not my name."

The second day the Queen tried nicknames—such as Spindleshanks, Knock-knees, and so on. To each one the little man shook his head. He answered, "That's not my name."

By the third morning, the Queen was in despair. She called the messenger to her.

"Alas, my lady, I have not heard any new names," the messenger said. "But I did have one odd adventure. As I came up a high hill at the edge of the forest, where the foxes and the hares bid each other good night, I saw a little house. In front of the house burned a little fire. Around

the fire danced a queer little man. He did not see me, for I stepped behind a tree. And the little man was singing:

> *"Today I scour, tomorrow I bake,*
> *And then the child I'll surely take.*
> *Little guesses the good dame*
> *That Rumpelstiltskin is my name."*

The Queen's joy at hearing this was great. She took a rich ruby ring off her finger and gave it to the messenger.

When the little man appeared, the Queen said, "Surely your name is Ebenezer!"

"No, that's not my name."

"Then your name must be Obediah."

"You asked me that the first day, my lady," said the little man, grinning. "Ah," she said timidly, "I don't suppose you could possibly be called Rumpelstiltskin."

"Some witch has told you that!" the little man screamed. In his rage, he stamped his foot so hard that it sank into the ground up to his waist. Then, in a passion, he seized his other foot with both hands and tore himself right in two.

When Our Country Was Younger

Open the album; see the faces
That stare from by-gone days and places.

The stern one is Great-grandpa Lear:
He was a whiskered pioneer.

Primly stands Great-great-aunt Bess:
She knew the Indians, I guess.

They look severe in beards and curls,
And yet they once were boys and girls.

—*Dorothy Hall*

Kitten-in-a-Basket

Elizabeth Coatsworth

Long ago, when America was young, there was a little spotted kitten named Nelly. She had extra toes on her front paws for good luck, and very pretty manners.

During her first weeks Nelly lived on a farm in a state called Pennsylvania. In the spring she noticed that everyone seemed very busy. A lot of people came and took off most of the furniture and the pigs and the cattle. At last only the four horses, the dog, one cow, a bull calf and Nelly were left.

Then, one morning at dawn, the young farmer and his wife rose up and packed everything they still owned on three of the horses. On the white mare they put a sort of saddle between two crates of chickens. The little girl, Hannah, and her mother took turns riding at the head of the procession on this horse, which wore a bell around her

224

neck. Wherever the bell-mare went, the other three horses would follow. In front of the horses went the young farmer, with his gun over his arm. He and the dog drove the cow and the calf before them up the trail.

As for Nelly, she saw all this through the cracks in the basket in which she traveled, sometimes in Hannah's lap and sometimes in the lap of Hannah's mother. At first she mewed and mewed with fright.

"Got to get rid of that yowling kitten," the farmer said. "Turn her loose, Hannah. She can still find her way back to the settlements."

But Hannah begged hard and said that she was sure that Nelly would soon quiet down. And Nelly did. She even came to like the rocking of the horse, and the smell of new country which came to her through the cracks of her basket. Often, when the family stopped to rest, she was let out and given warm milk to drink. She had no home any more, and cats love their homes. But soon Nelly adopted her basket as home. When Hannah called, she would jump in and settle down in a contented ball of fur and whiskers.

At night they sometimes slept in houses and sometimes beside the trail under the stars. Then Nelly snuggled close to Hannah when she heard the wolves howl. Every day they moved farther and farther west. At night, their meals were cooked over a fire beside the trail. The young farmer shot squirrels and rabbits. His wife cooked them in an iron pot which one of the horses carried. She made hoe cakes of corn meal close to the embers. Always there was milk. They moved slowly, in one direction, and even the kitten-in-the-basket enjoyed the life.

At last the trail began to climb up and up and up, among rocks, past loud waterfalls. At first all the animals were terrified, but after a while they became used to the mountains. Now there were almost no houses. When Nelly woke in the night, she sometimes saw that Hannah's father was sitting, listening, with his gun across his lap.

Once they met a family coming in the opposite direction.

The horses stopped and the two men talked.

"Don't go on to Kentucky," the stranger said. "There are too many Indians. Too many settlers are being killed. We had land there and a cabin built last fall. But we are coming back, where we can sleep at nights without being afraid."

"The land is good?" asked Hannah's father.

"Yes, but it is dark with blood."

Hannah's father glanced at her mother. She held her head up and smiled back at him.

"We're going on," he said.

So the two families parted on the trail.

After a while, Hannah's father and mother took turns sitting up with the gun, every night.

"Go to sleep, Hannah," they said. "We want to scare off any bears that might come to call on the kitten. Bears are so tame in these woods that they want to be invited for supper."

Hannah laughed. With her father and mother so near, she wasn't afraid. But Nelly crawled right up under Hannah's chin, and so they went to sleep.

After a while the trail began to wind down hill. Beyond them they could see a great valley, partly forested and partly open.

"Daniel Boone's country," said Hannah's

father. "We'll be at the fort soon. We'll settle somewhere near neighbors. The land is the best in America, they say."

But now he walked ahead of the cow and the calf, with his gun cradled on his arm. He looked to right and to left as he walked, trying to see into the shadows, to study every turn of the trail.

When the Indians Came

Yet when the Indians came, his gun was leaning against a tree a little way off and he was eating the drumstick of a wild turkey which he had shot a few days before. It was noonday, with the sun overhead—such a quiet, peaceful noonday.

There were four Indians, with paint on their faces and feathers in their hair, and long leather leggings. They came between the man and his gun. They looked at him and at the woman and the little girl. The dog growled, but Hannah's father ordered him to be quiet.

He smiled at the Indians and made signs of friendship. He invited them to eat turkey with him. They squatted down and ate, but always they kept between him and the gun. When they

laughed, it was to each other. Were they friendly, or did they mean trouble? It was hard to say.

Hannah had an idea. She took the basket in which Nelly was napping, and undid the catch which held the cover down. Then she pushed it into the center of the circle. "Here kitty, kitty," she called softly.

For a moment Nelly didn't stir. Then the top of the basket rose a little and Nelly's face appeared, peeking out. She had a round head and eyes of kitten-blue. The Indians had never seen a cat or a kitten before. They stared at the little round face. Pretty soon Nelly squirmed out of the basket and Hannah took a stick and played with her.

Nelly had never played so prettily. In no time at all the Indians were laughing with pleasure. They, too, took sticks and played with Nelly, and Nelly played with them. Then the man who appeared to be their chief rose, picked Nelly up, and held her on his bare arm. He nodded and smiled. The others, too, rose. They all made signs of friendship. The chief found an English word.

"Good," he said, and then he repeated, "Good."

"He's taking Nelly!" cried Hannah.

"Let him," her father said quickly. "We don't dare anger him."

"Indeed, he *shan't* take Nelly!" Hannah cried. She ran up to the Indian and pulled Nelly away from him. Then she faced him, her eyes sparkling and her cheeks red.

The Indians looked at her in surprise. Suddenly the chief laughed. He liked her courage.

"Good," he said again. "Good." And he and the others went off.

But another day the Indians came back, bringing deer meat. And once again they suddenly appeared when the horses were floundering in a swamp and Hannah's father needed help.

They were true friends to all Hannah's family, then and later when their cabin was built. But Hannah was their favorite. Hannah and her kitten, the kitten who had come to Kentucky in a basket. And later on, some of Nelly's own kittens went to live in the Indian camp. All the Indian children made a great fuss over them, and treated them as something very rare and wonderful.

Little Quekel Friends

Marguerite Henry and Wesley Dennis

Little Benjamin West was a Quaker boy of long ago. Unlike most Quakers of his day, Benjamin wanted to be a painter, and his cat Grimalkin seemed to sympathize with him.

Benjamin West was a real person. When he grew up, he did become a well-known American painter.

How still it was! Benjamin stopped a moment to listen to the stillness. And then he found that it was not still at all. A nut dropped with a bump at his feet. Bird wings whistled through the forest. And far off there was the crackling sound of fire. Benjamin smelled the wind in great excitement.

"The Indians! They must be firing the forest

to kill off the brush," he cried. "Make haste, Grimalkin!"

Grimalkin had stopped to sharpen his claws on a tree. He finished the job to his full satisfaction. Then he hurried after Benjamin. Benjamin broke into a run.

"I hope it is old Sassoonan!" he panted as he ran. "If it is, he will bake fish for thee, Grimalkin, and corn cakes for me."

Suddenly Benjamin burst full upon the Indians. The sight held him stock still. A great circle of fire was licking at the base of a white fir tree. And around the tree danced Chief Sassoonan and his three sons, Bear and Elk and Beaver. Each waved long poles with wet rags tied at the ends. Then, as soon as the fire leaped above a certain line on the tree trunk, they snuffed it out with the wet rags. There was a loud hissing sound as the water drowned the fire.

"Why," said Benjamin, "they are going to fell the tree and hollow out a boat!"

Quickly, Benjamin squatted down on the earth and began sketching them on his drawing board. As the Indian figures took shape, he frowned. "I long to paint them a good copper-brown," he said to Grimalkin.

Just then the Indians came running toward Benjamin, their voices raised in a cry. And to the crashing and snapping of branches, the fir tree fell to earth. Grimalkin, trembling in fear, leaped onto Benjamin's shoulder.

"Be not afraid, kitling," comforted Benjamin. "All will soon be quiet."

At that very moment, Sassoonan caught sight of the white boy and the black cat. His old face wrinkled with pleasure. He raised his hand in greeting.

"*Itah!*" he said, in a voice that seemed to come from the bottom of a well. "*Itah,* my little Quekel friends."

"And good be to thee, too!" laughed Benjamin, jumping to his feet.

Then, solemnly, the old Indian chief and the

Quaker lad shook hands. Grimalkin smelled the chief with approval. He liked the smell of bear's grease about him.

Meanwhile, Bear and Elk and Beaver had gathered about the drawing board. Their beady eyes never changed expression. For a long time they stared at the picture. Finally Sassoonan joined them. Taking the board in his hands he pointed to the tree that Benjamin had drawn.

"Is good," he said.

"Why, he says 'Good'!" said Benjamin. "Did thee hear that, Grimalkin?"

"Amen!" nodded Bear and Elk and Beaver.

Again Sassoonan picked up the board. This time he pointed to the Indians dancing around the fire. He shut his right fist and threw out his opened hand as if he were tossing away something very unpleasant.

His sons shouted and said, "Amen!" Benjamin was puzzled. Had he hurt Sassoonan's feelings?

For answer, Sassoonan made signs for Benjamin to pick up his drawing board and follow. Then he reached beneath some brush and drew out a deer-skin bag filled with bear's grease.

In a single file, Benjamin, with Grimalkin on his shoulder, and the three young Indians followed Sassoonan. Benjamin was not in the least afraid. Sassoonan was an old friend. Each year he came to the Inn with things to sell—baskets and brooms, venison meat and wild turkey, deerskin, bearskin, and beaver. Many times, Sassoonan's clan had raised their wigwams in Papa's orchard.

Now they were coming out on grassy land close to a stream. A bridge, made of a single tree trunk, lay across the stream. Sassoonan stooped low. He pointed to the bridge and then to his back. It was plain to see that he wanted to carry Benjamin pickaback, as he used to do when Benjamin was very small.

Benjamin blushed. He was much too big to ride pickaback now, but Sassoonan was chief of the Turtle Clan. It was a great honor to be carried by a chief. Besides, he could not offend Sassoonan. So, with Grimalkin still on his shoulder, he climbed onto Sassoonan's back.

When they reached the far bank, Bear began digging up handfuls of red earth. Beaver began digging up handfuls of yellow clay. Then, with a small stone and a large flat grinding slab, Bear and Beaver began to grind the lumps of earth. Elk was gathering mussel shells.

Beaver finished first. His red earth was pow-

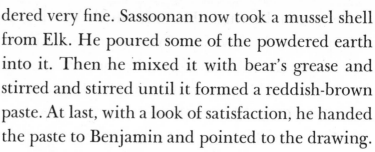

dered very fine. Sassoonan now took a mussel shell from Elk. He poured some of the powdered earth into it. Then he mixed it with bear's grease and stirred and stirred until it formed a reddish-brown paste. At last, with a look of satisfaction, he handed the paste to Benjamin and pointed to the drawing.

Benjamin dipped his finger into the color. It trembled a little as he painted the Indian figures a rich coppery red.

"Grimalkin!" he shouted. "At last I have color! Color! Color!"

Grimalkin acted as if he understood. He leaped several times into the air and mewed his approval.

"Amen! Amen! Amen!" the Indians cried.

A Painting Class

Suddenly they began stripping pieces of bark from trees near the water. Then they squatted on their heels and began to paint on the bark with the red and yellow colors they had made.

Benjamin watched openmouthed. Sassoonan was painting a turtle because he was chief of the Turtle Clan. The youngest Indian was painting

a beaver because his name meant beaver. The third Indian was painting a bear, and the fourth an elk.

What fascinated Benjamin was the way they laid on their colors. Beaver had chewed the stem of a tall spear of grass. He was using the chewed end exactly as if it were a goose-quill pen. Sassoonan was using a flat piece of wood that looked like a small butter paddle. And Elk was using a piece of bark.

"Think on it!" Benjamin whispered to Grimalkin. "The Indians like to draw, too. At last I've found some *real* schoolfellows."

The sun was directly overhead when the Indians went back to finish their boat. While Grimalkin sunned himself, Benjamin helped the Indians gather dry twigs to lay on top of the felled trunk. He helped set fire to them. After the fire had made a deep hollow in the trunk, Bear and Elk and Beaver scraped the inside surface with pieces of sharp stone.

"Little Quekel friends soon eat!" said Sassoonan. By this time the inside of the canoe was scraped as smooth as a stone. While corn cakes roasted in the burning tree stump, Bear and Elk and Beaver invited Benjamin to go fishing. With nothing but birds' claws for fish hooks, they caught eight sunfish and a red-bellied trout. Grimalkin had good luck, too. He caught a frog.

Afternoon found Benjamin and the Indians sitting on the floor of the forest, sharing their food. They ate until they could hold no more.

Sassoonan took a clay pipe out of the skin pouch hanging around his neck. He filled it with tobacco and puffed slowly. After a long silence, he spoke softly to his sons. At once they brought out their bows and arrows. They taught Benjamin how to shoot flying squirrels. Then they showed him how to make a sun sign. They drew a circle on the ground with a sharp stone and drove a twig into the center of the circle, bending it in the direction of the sun.

"I see!" nodded Benjamin. "If we should be scouts we could make a sun sign for our followers. It would tell them when we left here."

"Amen!" answered the Indians, pleased at the quickness of their pupil.

Suddenly Benjamin realized that the twig pointed to sunset time. He picked up his drawing board and whistled for Grimalkin.

"Run! Run!" spoke Sassoonan. "Cold night soon here. Good-by, little Quekel friends."

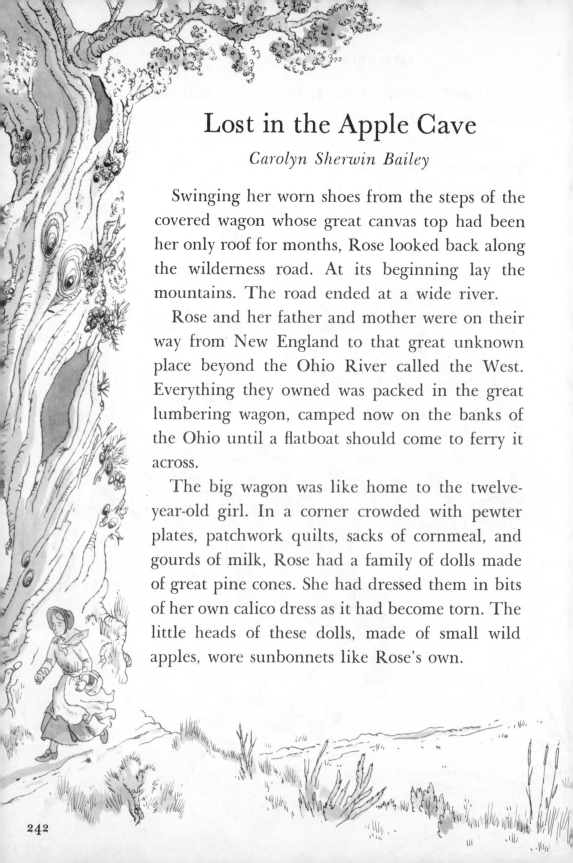

Lost in the Apple Cave

Carolyn Sherwin Bailey

Swinging her worn shoes from the steps of the covered wagon whose great canvas top had been her only roof for months, Rose looked back along the wilderness road. At its beginning lay the mountains. The road ended at a wide river.

Rose and her father and mother were on their way from New England to that great unknown place beyond the Ohio River called the West. Everything they owned was packed in the great lumbering wagon, camped now on the banks of the Ohio until a flatboat should come to ferry it across.

The big wagon was like home to the twelve-year-old girl. In a corner crowded with pewter plates, patchwork quilts, sacks of cornmeal, and gourds of milk, Rose had a family of dolls made of great pine cones. She had dressed them in bits of her own calico dress as it had become torn. The little heads of these dolls, made of small wild apples, wore sunbonnets like Rose's own.

Kicking her heels against the wagon step, Rose wished that she knew what lay within those deep woods at the right of their camp. She watched her mother bending over some knitting. Her father was trying to catch fish for supper. Rose stood up at last, swinging a little hand-made basket over her arm.

"I am going for a walk, Mother," she said. "Perhaps I can find some berries in the wood to eat with our porridge tonight."

"Do not go too far, Rose," her mother warned. "Your father saw a big brown bear quite close this morning."

"I will be back by supper time," Rose said.

In five minutes Rose was out of all sight and sound of the wagon camp. The faint stir of a passing snake among the fallen leaves in the forest, the patter of a chipmunk's little feet, the flapping of a crow's wings were the only sounds. Rose had never thought that she could lose the trail. But soon it seemed as if each moment she were going deeper into the wilderness. Her arms and legs were scratched by the bushes.

In the Cave

Rose ran. She clung to the little rush basket for comfort. It broke her fall as she stepped down, tumbled, and found herself a prisoner in a cave. The opening had been carefully screened by leafy branches and bushes. When she picked herself up and looked about, Rose could not believe her eyes.

The cave smelled deliciously of apples. Eating apples were a new fruit in those days, and rather rare. But here, in a roomy cave with a little bubbling spring at the back to keep the fruit moist, were shelves and shelves of wonderful apples, stored away for the winter. There were August apples. There were great Golden Pippins, hard little russet apples, and great red spicy apples. Choosing one of these apples, Rose sat down on the mossy floor to munch it. This might be a bear's cave, she thought, but it was a pleasant place.

Rose ate her apple down to its nest of big black seeds. She was just cupping her hands to drink from the spring, when a shadow darkened the door of the cave. Could it be the bear? Rose was frightened as she saw a dark form closing the opening. But a voice reassured her.

"Don't be afraid, little girl. It's only Appleseed Johnny. Welcome to my orchard!"

The man—strange indeed with his long hair, ragged clothes, and feet bare save for Indian moccasins—held out his hand to Rose.

"Come and see my trees, little girl," he said. "Come and see my house, too. Then I will show you the way to the camp again."

The man led Rose out of the cave and into a clearing where grew apple, cherry, peach, and plum trees. He was still a young man, but he said that he had traveled on foot to Pittsburgh all the long way from Springfield, in Massachusetts.

His name was John Chapman. He was called
Appleseed Johnny because he was the only
orchardman of the pioneers. He loved apples,
and he knew how much the West needed fruit.

Appleseed Johnny showed Rose the shed where
he sorted and washed apple seeds, and started
new trees. Then they went into the cabin he had
built for himself of logs of oak, chestnut, and
pine. The nails in the cedar door were handmade.
So was the star-shaped iron latch.

In the light of the big stone fireplace, the girl thought that Appleseed Johnny looked like an Indian—as brown, sharp-eyed, and slender. He gave a low call. Down from the shelf near the roof fluttered a sleepy little owl, to nestle on his shoulder.

"Folks say there are bears in these woods," said Rose.

Appleseed Johnny laughed. He went to the door and made an odd growling sound. Wide-eyed, Rose saw a shaggy brown animal lumber out of the gathering darkness, sniff at Appleseed Johnny, and then pass by.

Appleseed Johnny filled a big pewter mug with milk for Rose. He put a comb of golden honey and three red apples in her basket. Last, he gave her a little apple tree, no taller than her pine-cone doll, and a small deerskin bag of seeds.

"Now I will lead you to the edge of the woods," he said. "And when you come to your new home in the wilderness, set out this young apple tree in the sunshine. Water it. Build a little fence of brush about it to keep off the deer.

"In this bag are seeds of other apples, of berries, pears, cherries, grapes, plums, and peaches. Plant them and take care of them. Your mother will want berries and fruits for her pies, and jellies and jams for the winter. Your new home in the West will need grapevines growing over it, and a pink cloud of orchard blossoms in the spring."

As Appleseed Johnny talked, he led Rose safely through the darkening forest until she could see her own campfire and smell the fish her mother was cooking.

"Good-by, and thank you," she said.

"Good-by, Little Pioneer," he said. "Remember Appleseed Johnny and plant your trees."

"I will!" she called, as she ran over to hide her little tree and the seeds.

A flatboat was waiting for them in the morning. They drifted, wagon and all, over the Ohio River. Rose's covered wagon rolled on through the unsettled, wild country of Ohio. On, on went the wagon, until Rose's father found a farm site.

The seasons passed quickly. The land was cleared and a cabin built in two years. That was the year that Rose picked berries from the bushes that grew from Appleseed Johnny's seeds. In four years, roads were built, the cabin made larger, and Rose's dresses were longer. That was the year she first picked peaches, cherries, and plums from the trees planted from Appleseed Johnny's seeds.

In six years, Rose was a young lady. It was another October. The apples from Appleseed Johnny's little tree were in the kitchen, to be made into apple butter for the winter.

On linen thread, hanging from the beams of the kitchen, were strips of apples drying. The crane in the open fireplace held a brass kettle filled with peeled apples, with quinces and molasses added for flavor.

Rose would spend days preserving the apples. Down cellar, tubs of applesauce would freeze and keep through the winter as sweet as when it was made. The dried apples would be made into pies.

Appleseed Johnny Again

Rose stirred the apple butter, her back to the open door. Suddenly she heard a low call, like that of a little screech owl. Turning, she saw a surprising figure.

The man was as tall and straight as an Indian, and as keen-eyed. On his back he carried a great sack. He was as ragged as a beggar, and his hair had grown to his shoulders. He smiled at Rose. "You have grown, my child," he said.

"Appleseed Johnny!" she cried.

"Yes, I am Appleseed Johnny, still planting orchards in the wilderness. I gave away my house, and have been wandering for many years, scattering seeds, and teaching the pioneers how to plant and care for orchards."

"Come in," Rose begged. "Spend the night with us. These are your apples I am cooking. Your tree lived. Your seeds grew and gave us fruit."

An old letter tells us the rest of the story: how Appleseed Johnny spent the night in the cabin, made welcome by Roselle Rice and her family. In the morning he started on again. He carried a Bible in the sack with his seeds, and left one leaf of it with Rose. Then he tramped off into the woods farther West. She never saw him again.

Many covered-wagon children knew Appleseed Johnny, though Rose was the only one who wrote about him. But Appleseed Johnny walked for forty years, leaving at lonely cabins his little deer-skin bags of seeds and his Bible pages. He planted the orchards that now cover acres of the West.

Following the trail he started, great freight trains return now to the East carrying barrels of Jonathan, Winesap, Spitzenburg, Northern Spy, Delicious, King, Greening, and Golden Pippin apples for hungry boys and girls. The sturdy covered-wagon people, going West, gave this region its cities, its farms, its schools. And every pink apple blossom of the spring is scented with Appleseed Johnny's kindness to little Rose. Every bite of a rosy October apple tastes as sweet as those he laid away in his cave.

Sheep-Shearing

Laura Ingalls Wilder

Almanzo, a farmer boy, lived on a farm in New York State about eighty years ago. One of the spring tasks on the farm was sheep-shearing. Besides Almanzo and his older brother Royal, Father hired several men to make up the sheep-shearing crew.

The meadows and pastures were velvety with thick grass, and the weather was warm. It was time to shear sheep.

On a sunny morning, Pierre and Louis went with Almanzo into the pasture. They drove the sheep down to the washing-pen. The long pen ran from the grassy pasture into the clear deep water of Trout River. The pen had two gates opening into the pasture. Between the gates, a short fence ran to the water's edge.

Pierre and Louis kept the flock from running away, while Almanzo took hold of a woolly sheep and pushed it through one gate. In the pen, Father and Lazy John caught hold of it. Then Almanzo pushed another one through, and Royal and French Joe caught it. The other sheep stared and bleated, and the two sheep struggled and kicked and yelled. But the men rubbed their wool full of brown soft-soap and dragged them into the deep water.

There the sheep had to swim. The men stood waist-deep in the swift water, and held onto the sheep and scrubbed them well. The dirt came out of their wool and floated downstream with the soapsuds.

When the other sheep saw this, every one of

them cried, "Baa-aa-aa, baa-aa-aa!" and they all tried to run away. But Almanzo and Pierre and Louis ran yelling around the flock. They brought it back again to the gate.

As soon as a sheep was clean, the men made it swim around the end of the dividing fence, and they boosted it up the bank into the other side of the pen. The poor sheep came out bleating and dripping wet. But the sun soon dried it fluffy and white.

As fast as the men let go of one sheep, Almanzo pushed another into the pen, and they caught it and soaped it and dragged it into the river.

Washing sheep was fun for everybody but the sheep. The men splashed and shouted and laughed in the water, and the boys ran and shouted in the pasture. The sun was warm on their backs and the grass was cool under bare feet, and all their laughter was small in the wide, pleasant stillness of the green fields and meadows.

One sheep butted John. He sat down in the river and the water went over his head. Joe shouted, "Now if you had soap in your wool, John, you'd be ready for shearing!"

When evening came, all the sheep were washed. Clean and fluffy-white, they scattered up the slope, nibbling the grass. The pasture looked like a snowball bush in bloom.

Next morning John came before breakfast, and Father hurried Almanzo from the table. He took a wedge of apple pie and went out to the pasture, smelling the clover and eating the spicy apples and flaky crust in big mouthfuls. He licked his fingers. Then he rounded up the sheep and drove them across the dewy grass, into the sheepfold in the South Barn.

Father had cleaned the sheepfold and built a platform across one end of it. He and Lazy John each caught a sheep, set it up on the platform, and began cutting off its wool with long shears. The thick, white mat of wool peeled back, all in one piece. The sheep was left in bare pink skin.

With the last snick of the shears, the whole fleece fell on the platform. The naked sheep jumped off it, yelling, "Baa-aa-aa!" All the other sheep yelled back at the sight. But already Father and John were shearing two more.

Royal rolled the fleece tightly and tied it with twine. Almanzo carried the fleece upstairs and laid it on the loft floor. He ran upstairs and down again as fast as he could. But another fleece was always ready for him.

Father and Lazy John were good sheep-shearers. Their long shears snipped through the thick wool like lightning. They cut close to a sheep, but never cut its pink skin. This was a hard thing to do, because Father's sheep were prize Merinos. Merinos have the finest wool, but their skin lies in deep wrinkles, and it is hard to get all the wool without cutting them.

Keeping Up With Father

Almanzo was working fast, running upstairs with the fleeces. They were so heavy that he could carry only one at a time. He didn't mean to idle, but when he saw the tabby barn-cat hurrying past with a mouse, he knew she was taking it to her new kittens.

He ran after her. Far up under the eaves of the Big Barn he found the little nest in the hay, with four kittens in it. The tabby cat curled herself around them, loudly purring. The black slits in her eyes widened and narrowed and widened again. The kittens' tiny pink mouths uttered tiny meows. Their naked little paws had wee white claws, and their eyes were shut.

When Almanzo came back to the sheepfold, six fleeces were waiting. Father spoke to him sternly.

"Son," he said, "see to it you keep up with us after this."

"Yes, Father," Almanzo answered, hurrying. But he heard Lazy John say, "He can't do it. We'll be through before he is."

Then Father laughed and said, "That's so, John. He can't keep up with us."

Almanzo made up his mind to show them. If he hurried fast enough, he could keep up. Before noon he had caught up with Royal, and had to wait while a fleece was tied. So he said, "You see, I can keep up with you!"

"Oh no, you can't!" said John. "We'll beat you. We'll be through before you are. Wait and see." Then they all laughed at Almanzo.

They were laughing when they heard the dinner horn. Father and John finished the sheep they were shearing, and went to the house. Royal tied the last fleece and left it, and Almanzo still had to carry it upstairs. Now he understood what they meant. But he thought, "I won't let them beat me."

He found a short rope and tied it around the neck of a sheep that wasn't sheared. He led the sheep to the stairs. Then, step by step, he tugged and boosted her upward. She bleated all the way, but he got her into the loft. He tied her near the fleeces and gave her some hay to keep her quiet. Then he went to dinner.

All that afternoon, Lazy John and Royal kept telling him to hurry or they'd beat him. Almanzo answered, "No, you won't. I can keep up with you."

Then they laughed at him.

He snatched up every fleece as soon as Royal tied it, and hurried upstairs and ran down again. They laughed to see him hurrying. They kept saying, "Oh no, you won't beat us! We'll be through first!"

Just before chore-time, Father and John raced to shear the last two sheep. Father beat. Almanzo ran with the fleece, and was back before the last

one was ready. Royal tied it. Then he said, "We're all through! Almanzo, we beat you! We beat you!" Royal and John burst into a great roar of laughter, and even Father laughed.

Then Almanzo said, "No, you haven't beat me. I've got a fleece upstairs that you haven't sheared yet."

They stopped laughing, surprised. At that very minute the sheep in the loft, hearing all the other sheep let out to pasture, cried, "Baa-aa-aa!"

Almanzo shouted, "There's the fleece! I've got it upstairs and you haven't sheared it! I beat you! I beat you!"

John and Royal looked so funny that Almanzo couldn't stop laughing. Father then roared with laughter.

"The joke's on you, John!" Father shouted. "He laughs best who laughs last!"

Betsy's New Hat

Carolyn Sherwin Bailey

Trot-trot-trot! "I'm happy, happy, happy!" Betsy Metcalf's happy heart kept time to the beat of her horse's hoofs as she rode, side-saddle, into town. She had the week's supply of butter and eggs from her father's farm for the Providence market.

She was an odd little figure. Twelve years old in the year 1799, Betsy was a country lass who lived on the other side of Smith's Hill from Providence. Her starched blue-calico dress and white apron stood stiffly out over the saddle. Her big sunbonnet did its best to hide the bright curls.

In her pannier-baskets, carefully balanced on either side of the saddle, white eggs, round yellow cheeses, and pats of golden butter wrapped in grape leaves were packed in moss. Betsy stopped a moment on the top of Smith's Hill.

Beyond the river that lapped the Parade and Town Wharf shone the blue waters of Narragansett Bay. Along the Parade and the length of the curved waterfront were many shops. Their gaily painted wooden signs flapped in the wind.

The shipyards were there, too, and there stood Jacob Whitman's smithy. Whitman, the smith, exchanged horseshoes and ironware with the shoemakers of near-by Lynn. "Gloshes, Clogs, Shoos," said his sign, and Betsy looked at her own well-worn shoes. But it was not a pair of two-shilling shoes for which she longed, but something much more exciting.

The sound of a drum came to her. As she came trotting along the main street of Providence, she had to pull her horse in sharply to give the road to the town crier. He marched along, drumming, and calling in a clear voice, "Organ music Saturday night in Kings Church! Come one, come all!"

A great organ with two hundred pipes had been brought from England in 1772 to Kings Church in Providence. Betsy's mother had told her how wicked the deacons had at first thought this idea of organ music in church.

Now the crier's words gave Betsy an added joy in the day's marketing. A girl of twelve would feel ashamed to wear a calico sunbonnet to Kings Church for the organ music. She was going to buy herself a new bonnet.

"Make speed, Dobbin!" she said. They came at last to the public market. There, bargaining housewives and shrewd farmers, hissing geese, and wagons loaded with fruit and vegetables showed that this was the Providence market day.

Betsy dismounted and tied her horse to a post. She went in and out of the crowd with her baskets. "Fresh butter. Large eggs. Rich cheese," she called.

Carefully, Betsy put the shillings in her pocket. She gave Dobbin the oats that she had brought in a saddlebag. She ate her lunch, an apple turnover and a piece of cheese, in the shade of a tree. Then she started upon her shopping adventure.

She looked in the window of a bookshop. Almanacs, spelling books, and books of hymns were for sale. Also, the storekeepers Ephraim and Jabez Nightingale were selling something new, called "Powder for Preserving the Teeth."

But Betsy turned back to the little street of shops called Cheapside. She found a shop that sold bright English prints for dresses, lawn from India as thin and soft as a summer cloud, "taffaties," and other fabrics of silk and wool that our fast sailing ships were bringing from far-off lands.

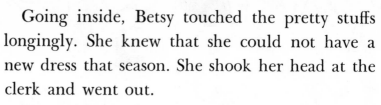

Going inside, Betsy touched the pretty stuffs longingly. She knew that she could not have a new dress that season. She shook her head at the clerk and went out.

Betsy skipped from one shop to another until she came to the shop called "The Sign of the Hat." Here she went in.

Stone crocks for holding the winter's jams and pickles, jars of pepper and spices, sacks of flour, cakes of chocolate, and strong-smelling Cheshire cheese were heaped around the bonnets. But Betsy went straight to that part of the shop where her dream lay. On a table, quite alone, was a beautiful imported straw bonnet. It was wide-brimmed like a hat, and trimmed with ribbon and flowers.

Betsy clasped her hands as she stood admiring it. She fancied herself walking grandly into Kings Church in that straw bonnet for the organ music. The shopkeeper came out of a corner, lifted the bonnet, and turned it about.

"Good Master Balch, how much is it?" Betsy asked.

Nathan Balch, the owner of "The Sign of the Hat," sighed. "One pound," he said. "And I shall

never be able to sell it this season at that price.
It came by ship to Providence, the only straw
bonnet in the town, but too costly."

One whole pound! And Betsy's mother had
said that she might spend one shilling of the
market money for herself.

Betsy pulled her sunbonnet down over her eyes to hide her tears as she went out of the shop. She found Dobbin, untied him, and rode slowly home with her empty panniers.

Betsy's Bonnet

It was nearly sunset as Betsy rode home along the farm road. As she put Dobbin in his stall, the reapers came into the barn with great bundles of oats upon their shoulders. Some of the straw dropped to the barn floor. Betsy gathered it up. It was golden yellow, soft, and pliable. Why, she suddenly saw that this common field straw was as pretty as the straw from which the beautiful Providence bonnet was made!

Betsy sat down in the late sunshine of the barn door. She carefully split the straw with her fingers. She wove it into a braid. Before supper time Betsy had made quite a bundle of straw braid. After supper she began sewing it into the shape of a bonnet, with a wide brim to tie under her chin.

Saturday night Dobbin made another trip, with Betsy and her mother on his back. They were riding into Providence for the organ music at

Kings Church. A very smart and beautiful Betsy now! She wore her best pink-calico dress with white ruffles at the neck and sleeves. A homespun cloak covered it from the dust of the road. As she dismounted and went into church, not even the great ladies who had arrived by coach could boast of so stylish a bonnet.

Its wide brim was tied under the little girl's chin with cherry-colored ribbons dyed in the home dye-pot. About the low crown lay rosy everlasting flowers, also gathered and dyed by Betsy.

Betsy Metcalf's straw bonnet was the talk of that long-ago evening in old Providence. She was surprised the next day to receive a letter from Master Balch himself, begging for directions for making hat-braid from straw. During all that winter, Betsy and the other Providence girls were busy making the straw braid that was sewed into bonnets for the coming spring. The straw was split into seven strands and braided. Bobbins were used for quicker braiding, and the girls carried their bundles of straw about with them. The art of making straw bonnets became as much the style as knitting.

Betsy Metcalf became famous. Old records tell us that orders for her straw bonnets came from forty miles around Providence. No other hats were so well liked in New England as hers. Sunbonnets and hoods were quickly forgotten. After a while, boys and men took up the fashion of the straw hat. Hat factories opened all over New England.

The story of twelve-year-old Betsy Metcalf of Providence comes to us from neighbors who knew about the first straw hat she made. She kept up her work all her life. When she was eighty she was still making hats. We might not have had our hat factories, hat shops, and new hats for Easter, if a little girl in a sunbonnet so many years ago had not made up her mind to make the best of things.

Tales That Grew Tall

I went to the corner
   to buy me some bread—
And there, at the corner,
   I met me a bear
As big as a bus,
   with a cold in his head;
He sneezed, and the store
   sailed away in the air!

I said to the bear,
   "Use Stopasneez Salve!"
Toward purchasing same
   he made not a motion—
So I grabbed the long tail
   that the beast didn't have
And swung him far into
   the *At*-lantic Ocean!

          —*Dorothy Hall*

Cats for Kansas

LeGrand

Once there were no cats in Kansas. In those days, there were buffalo in Kansas. And there were Indians in Kansas. And there were some settlers in Kansas. Old Gabe Slade, the trader, was there, too. But there were no cats in Kansas.

That was a sad thing for the settlers. Back East, where they came from, there had always been cats to purr around the fireplace and catch the mice and make the house look cozy.

One day, Mrs. Gabe Slade said, "Gabe Slade, I want a cat. The Jenkinses want a cat. The Smiths want a cat. The Allens want a cat. The Stewarts want a cat. And the Joe Greens want a cat. All the settlers in Kansas want a cat. And there are no cats in Kansas."

Gabe Slade, old Gabe Slade, the trader, had an idea. He said, "I will go back East and get some cats. I will bring these cats to Kansas and trade them to the settlers. Then everybody's house will be home-sweet-home and folks will be happy in Kansas."

So he hitched up his oxen to his covered wagon and he drove across the prairies to the railroad. He took a train to the river. Then he went East on Captain Hank Hay's steamboat.

In the East, old Gabe Slade found all the cats he needed. He found black cats and white cats and striped cats and calico cats. He put all these cats into a big wooden crate. He loaded the crate on Captain Hank Hay's steamboat and started back to Kansas.

It was a very dark night, and Gabe Slade said, "Captain Hank, how can you see to steer this steamboat through the darkness?"

Captain Hank said, "On a dark night, I steer by sound. I steer by the sound of dogs barking along the shore. I know every dog on the river and I just steer from dog to dog."

Captain Hank listened hard. He said, "There

should be a yellow hound dog named William right about here. William barks like a bugle and he always barks when he hears a steamboat."

Gabe Slade and Captain Hank listened, but they heard no bark like a bugle. Captain Hank said, "Maybe William is asleep."

Then Gabe Slade had an idea. He got a fishhook and a line and started to fish in the river.

Captain Hank said, "Gabe Slade, this is no time for fishing. This is a time to listen for a yellow hound dog named William."

Gabe Slade went on with his fishing. He pulled in his line and he had a fish. He took the fish off

the hook and carried it to his cats. The cats were hungry. They made the kind of noise that hungry cats make when they see a fish.

And the noise woke the yellow hound dog whose name was William. He heard the cats and he started to bark. He barked like a bugle.

Captain Hank heard William. He said, "Now I know where I am." And he started the steamboat.

All the dogs along the river heard Gabe Slade's cats. They all barked, and Captain Hank steered from dog to dog. And that was how the steamboat got to the railroad by morning.

Gabe Slade put his crate of cats on a train. Then he climbed aboard and started out across the prairies to where he had left his covered wagon.

But there were Indians on the prairies in those days. And the Indians did not like the trains, because the trains scared the buffalo and spoiled the Indians' hunting. So the Indians decided to stop the trains.

They took a long rope and they stretched it across the railroad tracks. They pulled the rope tight when they saw a train coming. It was the train Gabe Slade and his cats were on.

Gabe Slade looked out. He saw the rope and he saw the Indians. He shouted to the engineer. "Boil up a little more steam," he shouted. "Get her boiling good and hard. This train must go through, because it's carrying cats for Kansas."

The Train Goes Through

The engineer boiled up as much steam as there was. He went ahead, and the train hit the rope.

The Indians held onto the rope. Then the air was full of Indians. Indians flew to the right, and Indians flew to the left. Indians flew up, and then they flew down. And feathers flew all around. And the train went through.

The train went on to where Gabe Slade had left his covered wagon. Gabe put his cats in the covered wagon and he started out across the prairie.

Then, one day, one of the oxen was sick. It was too sick to pull the covered wagon. It took two oxen to pull the covered wagon. And now Gabe Slade had only one. One was not enough.

Gabe Slade sat and he thought. He thought and he sat. He saw some buffalo running across the prairie. "Mm," he said. "A buffalo is a lot like an ox."

Gabe Slade took a rope and he made a lasso. He went out and lassoed a buffalo. The buffalo dragged Gabe Slade all over the prairie. It dragged him over the high ground, and it dragged him over the low ground. It dragged him across a little stream. There were a few trees beside the stream. Gabe Slade tied his rope around a fallen tree.

"There," he said. "I guess that will hold you."

But the buffalo was a very wild buffalo. And he was a very strong buffalo. He dragged the tree across the prairie. The tree had strong branches. The branches dug into the ground like a plow.

The buffalo ran. He turned and he ran. And as he ran, he plowed. He plowed up about a hundred and seven acres. Then he was tired. And when he was tired, he was tamed.

"Well, I do declare," Gabe Slade said. "Now I have a tame buffalo and a hundred and seven

acres of good farm land all plowed and ready to plant."

But still the settlers in Kansas had no cats.

Gabe Slade hitched up the tamed buffalo to the covered wagon, along with the good ox. And he drove his covered wagon across the prairie until he came to the place where the settlers lived, the settlers who had no cats.

And when Gabe Slade got there he traded his cats. He traded them to the Jenkinses . . . and the Smiths . . . and the Allens . . . and the Stewarts . . . and the Joe Greens. And to all the other settlers who had no cats.

Then all the settlers had cats to purr around the fireplace and catch mice and make the house look cozy. Everybody's house was home-sweet-home.

Old Gabe Slade was happy, too. He traded the cats for seeds. Then he planted the seeds in the hundred-and-seven acres of land that the buffalo had plowed.

And that was how Gabe Slade came to have a hundred-and-seven-acre farm, a tame buffalo, and a calico cat. And that was how cats came to Kansas.

Amazing Ships and Sailors

James V. Williams

That Famous River Boat, the Galusha

You do not see river steamboats like the old *Galusha,* nowadays. The *Galusha* was the biggest, fastest, and strongest steamboat ever to sail on the Ohio River.

The *Galusha* was driven by a paddlewheel at the back. This wheel was as big as twenty Ferris wheels put side by side. Standing on the deck, a man could just see the tops of the *Galusha's* smokestacks on a clear day. These smokestacks were pulled down like telescopes to let the *Galusha* go under a bridge.

The *Galusha's* whistle was so loud it was blown only in great emergencies. Its toot jarred the nails loose in houses twenty miles away.

The *Galusha's* most famous trip was the one that blew the feathers from pigs along the Ohio River. In the old days, pigs in the Ohio Valley had feathers, just like turkeys, chickens, and ducks. But not any more. And the *Galusha* is the reason why.

One day the *Galusha* was at Pittsburgh. Just as a cargo of new doughnut holes was being loaded on the boat, the captain got a message. It told him that a sudden rain was raising the Ohio River between Pittsburgh and Cincinnati. In order to get under the bridges, the *Galusha* would have to reach Cincinnati in exactly one hour and seventeen minutes.

The distance between Pittsburgh and Cincinnati is four hundred sixty-eight miles. No other boat had ever gone that distance in less than twenty-four hours. But the captain of the *Galusha* made up his mind to try. If he stayed at Pittsburgh, the doughnut holes might spoil.

The *Galusha* backed slowly out into the Ohio River. Then the captain ordered, "Full steam ahead!" The fires roared under the boilers. Smoke poured from the smokestacks like water from a firehose. The big paddlewheels beat the river into foam. The sun shining on the spray made a rainbow that passed all the way over Pittsburgh.

The *Galusha* shot down the river like lightning that was late getting started. The boat went so fast it scorched the water in the river.

When the *Galusha* was halfway to Cincinnati, the captain looked at his watch. A whole hour had passed! Any other boat captain might have given up. But not the *Galusha's* captain. He ordered more steam. The fires roared louder than ever. More smoke rolled from the smokestacks. In fact, the smoke coming from the smokestacks slowed down the sun, as thick mud slows down an auto. The sun had to shift into low gear to get through that smoke at all.

But while the sun slowed down, the *Galusha* raced faster than ever. The paddlewheel whirled faster than an electric fan. It made such a wind that it blew the feathers off every pig in the Ohio Valley. The turkeys, chickens, and ducks did not lose their feathers, because they turned and faced the wind. The wind just made their feathers lie down flat.

But the pigs were not so smart. They turned away from the wind. It peeled their feathers right off over their heads.

The *Galusha* reached Cincinnati in plenty of time. But to this day, you will very seldom see a pig with feathers in the Ohio Valley.

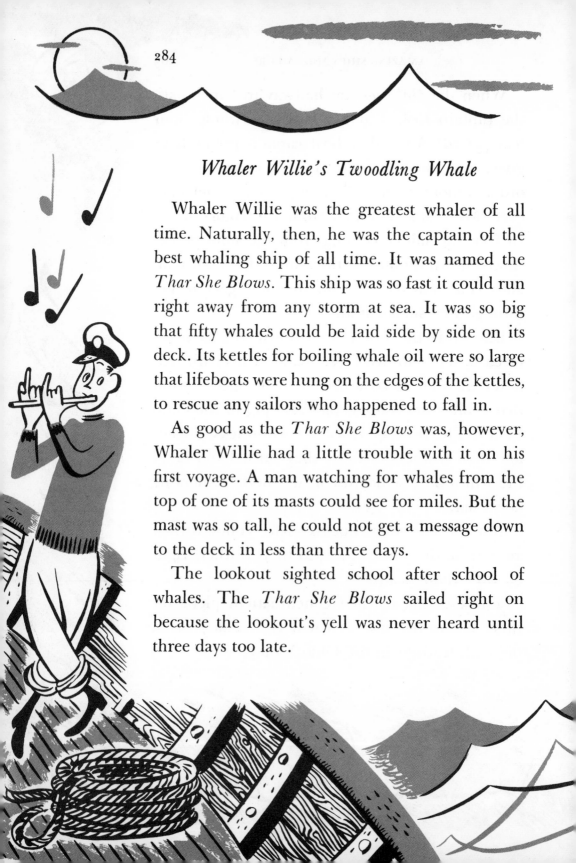

Whaler Willie's Twoodling Whale

Whaler Willie was the greatest whaler of all time. Naturally, then, he was the captain of the best whaling ship of all time. It was named the *Thar She Blows*. This ship was so fast it could run right away from any storm at sea. It was so big that fifty whales could be laid side by side on its deck. Its kettles for boiling whale oil were so large that lifeboats were hung on the edges of the kettles, to rescue any sailors who happened to fall in.

As good as the *Thar She Blows* was, however, Whaler Willie had a little trouble with it on his first voyage. A man watching for whales from the top of one of its masts could see for miles. But the mast was so tall, he could not get a message down to the deck in less than three days.

The lookout sighted school after school of whales. The *Thar She Blows* sailed right on because the lookout's yell was never heard until three days too late.

Whaler Willie went to his cabin to think. He thought without stopping for seven days and seven nights. When he came out, he carried his piccolo. He always took his piccolo on long voyages to play when he could not sleep.

Whaler Willie walked straight to the bow of his ship. He stood there and began playing.

"Twoodle-tweedle-eedle," went the piccolo.

He twoodled and tweedled for five hours. Just as the sun was setting, a whale broke from the water in front of the ship.

The crew rushed for the harpoons. But Captain Willie waved them back. He twoodled and tweedled some more. The whale clearly was fond of music. It rolled on its back. It smiled and chuckled. It waved its tail in time with the twoodles. It clapped its fins at every tweedle. Whenever Whaler Willie stopped for breath, the whale sighed. Big tears rolled from its eyes.

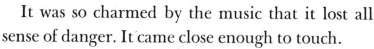

It was so charmed by the music that it lost all sense of danger. It came close enough to touch.

Quicker than a lightning flash, Whaler Willie thrust his piccolo into the blow hole on top of the whale's head. He seized an oar and hammered that piccolo in tight.

The whale shook and stood on its head. The piccolo stuck fast. The whale sneezed and snorted. Ear-splitting twoodles and tweedles came from its blow hole. The piccolo would not come out.

The whale went bounding over the sea like a rabbit, twoodling with every jump. It was out of sight long before it was out of hearing.

From then on, Whaler Willie had no more lookout trouble. He did not need a lookout. All he needed was a listener. He just listened for a twoodling and tweedling. Then he followed the sound to a school of whales. When one school was stowed away on the *Thar She Blows,* the twoodling whale joined another school.

No doubt, when there is just one whale left in the ocean, it will run from ships with a sad "Twoodle-tweedle-eedle."

The Bear and the Wildcat

Ellis Credle

Hank Huggins was long and lean and rangy. Folks said he told the tallest tales of anyone in the Blue Ridge Mountains. Hank always swore his stories were true—every word.

"Things just happen to me," he said. "Peculiar happenstances swarm after me like flies after a barrel of molasses. Why, just buying a little piece of beefsteak once got me into the worst predicament ever heard tell of!" Hank settled himself and began his tale.

* * *

It happened when I was a-living over on the other side of Thunderhead Mountain. It was a far piece from there down to Ashevilletown. In the fall of that year, after my apples were ripe, I loaded two bags full onto the old mule's back and rode on down to sell 'em.

I got there all right and got a pocket full of cash money for my load. I bought me a few things I needed, salt and nails and what-not. Then I said to myself, "Now what can I buy to pleasure my old lady?" It came to me, of a sudden, that she hadn't had a taste of beefsteak in a coon's age. I went into a butcher shop and had 'em cut me off a hunk. I put it in one of my saddlebags and off I set for home.

Now it's a long pull up and over old Thunderhead. The road is rocky and sometimes there's no road at all—you have to splash along the creek bed. And it's wild and lonesome all the way. Well, sir, along towards dark, the mule began to act skeery and skittish-like.

"Some varmint's got wind of this piece of fresh meat!" I said to myself. "Something's slipping through these bushes sure as shooting!"

I hadn't more than got the words out of my mouth than up on a limb over the road I caught sight of a wildcat fixed for a spring. Now a wildcat's not very big—not much heftier than a housecat. But let me tell you there's not a more ferocious critter in the entire length of the Blue Ridge

country! With those hind claws of his, he can
strip a man to ribbons in five minutes.

Well, sir, the same minute I got sight of *him,* I
heard a roar from the other side of the road. I
looked that-a-way. Jumping Jehoshaphat, there
was the biggest, blackest bear I ever laid eyes on!

He made a spring for me, his mouth wide open. The wildcat sprang toward me from the other side. I ducked, the mule leaped. It was a clean miss! I was getting away from there lickety-split when I heard a great scratching and scrambling behind. I glanced back and I'll be blessed if that wildcat hadn't leaped head first right into the bear's open mouth. His head was stuck tight. There they were, a-rolling and a-tumbling. The bear was a-choking and the wildcat was a-stifling to death.

The upshot of it was, I got home with the beefsteak, a wildcat, and a two-hundred-pound bear on my mule's back. My old lady made me a fur cap out of the cat skin. We got a fur robe big enough for a bed cover out of the bear hide. There was enough bear meat to feed a hundred and fifty people. So I broiled him over the coals and invited everybody within gunshot to come and help eat him up!

Building the Rockies

Glen Rounds

Paul Bunyan—Ol' Paul—was the mightiest logger who ever lived. In fact, he invented logging. With his big blue ox, Babe, Paul did many chores that our country needed to have done. One of his most helpful jobs was building the Rocky Mountains.

A couple of years after Ol' Paul finished logging off the Great Plains to serve as grazing land for the buffalo, he gets a letter from the King of Sweden. The King says as how he has more Swedes

than he has room for over there. He wonders if Paul knows of any place where he can send some of them.

Right away, Ol' Paul thinks of North Dakota and Minnesota. He writes the King a letter describing the two places. The King writes back that Minnesota sounds fine. But he wants North Dakota logged off, so his people can raise wheat. Also, he wonders if the hills could be taken off. These folks have been raised near the water. They are used to being able to see a long way.

. After a good deal of writing back and forth, they come to some kind of an agreement. By the time the first snow falls, Paul's all ready to start work.

Besides his regular woods crew, he has seven axmen that the King of Sweden sent over to help out. They're not much for looks. But before the winter's over, their fame has spread all through the timber country. They are huge fellows, and all brothers, and have worked out a system of their own for cutting trees. They work side by side going up hill, mowing down trees twenty-five at a swing.

Of course, by the time they reach the top of the hill, their axes are mighty dull. But instead of going back to camp to grind them, the men each pick out a big rock at the top and start it rolling. As it rolls and leaps down the hill, they follow, taking enormous steps and grinding their axes as they run.

With a crew like this, work goes on at a great rate. By spring, the whole country is logged off, and the slashings piled up ready to burn.

In the meantime, Ol' Paul and the King have been doing quite a lot of writing back and forth. The King offers Paul a bonus to drive the logs to Sweden. He makes a side bet of a dollar and a half that it can't be done. Paul says as how his men can drive logs anywhere. So he puts his best river crew on the job, with Shot Gunderson in charge.

Ol' Paul goes with them through the Great Lakes. He helps them get the drive down Niagara Falls. This is really quite a chore, as the falls were much higher then than they are now. But they get the entire drive over in three days and never lose a log.

The trip down the rest of the St. Lawrence River and across the Atlantic is simple. They make it in three weeks, even though they have to stop in the English Channel while the King comes out in a rowboat to see what an American log drive looks like.

While the men are gone with the logs, Ol' Paul's been busy getting rid of the hills. He has Ole build a big sledge hammer. Then he pounds the hills out flat as flapjacks. When that's done, he cuts some of the rivers down to creeks. He runs

them here and there to make the country look nice. Then he writes the King of Sweden to send over one of his Prime Ministers to O.K. the job.

Mountains Made to Order

A few months later, the King's favorite Prime Minister arrives. Paul has one of his men drive him out over the country in a wagon. And it is really a beautiful job. As far as the eye can see is rich, flat land covered with long green grass. The Prime Minister is pleased except for one thing.

At that time, there were no mountains between the Dakotas and the Pacific. In the winter, the winds blowing in from Siberia made the country mighty cold. So the Prime Minister tells Paul that he will have to put up some sort of a windbreak.

That kind of puts Ol' Paul up a stump. A thing of that size is a pretty big order even for him. But he goes over and studies the lay of the land and figures a while. It's plain to be seen that a regular board fence will not do. It'll cost a fortune just to keep it in repair, even if he can build one high enough to do any good.

While out looking the country over, he finds a deserted prairie-dog town. Now Ol' Paul always has an eye out for anything new that he can use in his business. So he pulls a few of the old prairie-dog holes up and takes them back to camp, intending to saw them up for postholes or something.

That night, however, he's watching Sourdough Sam setting his sourdough for next morning, when he gets an idea that is one of the best he ever had. He doesn't explain it to anyone. But he has a small cookshack built on sled runners, with holes in the bottom.

The next morning, he has Sam move his sourdough crocks and part of his helpers into the shack. Then he hitches Babe onto the outfit and hauls it out to the prairie-dog town. When they

get there, he drives along slower. Sam and the helpers get busy. They fill up the prairie-dog holes with sourdough, pouring it into them through the holes in the floor. Ole, the Big Swede, follows and plugs the holes with blocks of wood after they're filled.

It takes them most all day to work their way down from Alaska to New Mexico. But when they finish, every hole is filled clear to the top. If you've ever met up with sourdough, you can imagine what happens when all that sourdough starts to rise. The ground heaves for days. Big cracks show up on the prairie. Great rocks are pushed up. Inside of a week there's as fine a range of mountains as anyone could wish for, standing where the old prairie-dog town used to be.

The King of Sweden is so pleased that he sends Paul a bonus of two dollars along with the check for the job.

That sourdough hasn't quit working yet, especially out around the Jackson Hole country. There it can be heard gurgling and rumbling around under the ground, and now and then causing water to shoot up to a great height.

Old Paul

Where the tree-line scrapes the skyline
   And the Western mountains stand,
I seem to see Paul Bunyan
   Striding out across the land.

His eyes are like the lightning,
   His beard is like a cloud,
And his laughter is the thunder
   When thunder laughs out loud.

Oh, he built the Rocky Mountains
   And he shoveled out the Lakes
And he cut a lot of timber—
   He had everything it takes.

He loved the land he fashioned
   And his spirit marches still
In each purple sunset shadow
   Marching from each purple hill.

And I think—to see him striding
   Along the mountains' rim—
Our land's the only country
   That is big enough for him.

—Dorothy Hall

Febold Feboldson and His Remarkable Animals

Retold by Anne Malcolmson

Originally, Febold Feboldson had been a lumberjack for Paul Bunyan. He worked for Paul at the time the great lumber boss filled his camp with Swedes.

Soon Febold moved to Nebraska and started to work on his own. He did very well for a time, too, until his bad luck got the upper hand. Poor old Febold! He was a kind-hearted, gentle fellow who meant well. But nothing ever turned out right for him.

Febold had a marvelous collection of animals. The first of these strange beasts was the hide-behind. No one has ever seen one, not even Febold. It made a practice of hiding behind the loggers when they worked in the woods. No matter how quickly they turned around, the hide-behind turned just as quickly. There it was, hiding behind them and looking over their shoulders.

The only way that a logger could rid himself of the troublesome creature was to find a filla-ma-loo bird. This bird flew backwards over the logger's head. No hide-behind could stand to be seen by the filla-ma-loo bird, and so the logger could work in peace.

Then there was the hodag, sometimes called the

huggag. Paul Bunyan had sent the first of these to Febold in the hope that it might help him get rid of the coyotes. This beast had been bred on Pinnacle Mountain. In order to live on the mountain, the hodag had two short legs and two long ones. Out on the flat plains of Nebraska, the poor things were unable to stand up.

The coyotes finally met their match in the whimpering whingdings. The coyote, as you may know, is a sad creature. He sits on his haunches and bays at the moon as though his heart will break. Febold thought that the best way to get rid of them was to finish the job and break their hearts.

The whingdings did it. Their whimper was heart-breaking, all right! It was a cross between the bellow of a spanked baby and the yip of a hurt puppy. The whingdings gathered beside the Dismal River and whimpered until the coyotes felt so bad they sneaked off into the Colorado Mountains and haven't been heard from since.

After the whimpering whingdings came the happy auger. A gay, light-hearted creature he was. He looked something like a kangaroo with a corkscrew for a tail. His job was to bore post holes.

As you know, the ground in Nebraska is terribly hard. It's almost impossible to bore a hole for a fencepost. Febold tried the auger. The poor animal was gun-shy, so Febold crept up behind him and fired his six-shooter into the air. The auger was so frightened he jumped up six feet and landed on his tail. The corkscrew bored into the earth and made a perfect post hole.

Alas! One of Feboldson's neighbors bought a machine gun in Kansas City. He fired it at the auger to see him jump. The *ra-ta-tat-tat* of the gun scared the wits out of the animal. He leapt into the air twenty feet at a leap until he disappeared over the Rockies.

The most useful animal Febold ever developed

was the beeline ox. He had been given the job of straightening the line between Kansas and Nebraska. At first he was stumped. He plowed a furrow with his oxen, but the furrow was crooked. Then he crossed the oxen with a bee. A bee always flies in a straight line. When he had produced a perfect bee-ox, he hitched it to the plow and tried again. This time the furrow was straight—a real beeline, as you can see on the map.

The Petrified Snow and After

In spite of his success with birds and animals, poor Febold Feboldson was pretty much of a failure in other ways. He bought a prairie wagon and a team of oxen and spent several years carrying pioneers across the Western wilderness to the gold rush of California. He did well at this until the year of the Petrified Snow.

The snow swept down and covered the whole state of Nebraska. Then it turned to stone. Traveling was impossible, and Febold, who made his living traveling, was having a very hard time of it. None of the pioneers would budge from the tavern stoves in Kansas City.

At last, he drove out to the Arizona Desert and filled his wagon with its burning sand. This he carted back and poured on top of the stony snow. The heat from the sand melted the hard stuff and warmed the air. Soon Febold's customers got up from their firesides and agreed to hire him again. A great success, he thought.

He was wrong. When he returned from California, he found that the sand had burned right through the snow to the ground. It had burned away all the trees and shrubs in the whole state. Nothing would grow at all.

When the kind-hearted soul saw what he had done to his dear Nebraska, he was wretched. He built himself a little sod shanty on the banks of the Dismal River. He tried to urge the pioneers to stop there, and make their homes in Nebraska.

But the people wouldn't stop. They had their hearts set on the gold to be found in California.

Then Febold sent to Peru for a cargo of goldfish. He dumped these into the Dismal River one dark night. The next day he ran out to the rolling wagon trains. "Stop! Stop!" he cried. "I have found gold in the rushing streams of this beautiful state of Nebraska!"

The word "Gold!" caught the pioneers' attention. They stopped their wagons and rushed to the riverbank. Eagerly they dipped their pans into the stream. The flashing of the fish looked like the gleam of a thousand gold flakes. But when the pans were lifted out of the water, there was no metal in them. Nothing but fish scales! The gold-crazy pioneers were furious and kicked Febold for all his pains.

After his goldfish plan had failed, Febold tried to do something about the grasshoppers. Along with the burning sand from the Arizona Desert had come thousands of the insects. What the sands didn't burn, the grasshoppers ate.

He heard that flying fish liked to eat them, so he brought in a school of the lovely silvery things. The fish ate the grasshoppers, but the fish were worse than the insects. The skies were full of them.

Now Febold had to do something about the fish. He brought in timber wolves to eat the fish. The wolves did what they were meant to do. But without any timber around they became homesick. They spent their time howling. The noise drove people away.

At last, Febold stopped trying to mend his mistakes. He went back to his shack on the Dismal River and sat down to think. If only he could find something that would bring back the green grass and waving grain to his dear Nebraska!

The next moment he had the right answer. Rain! If he could make it rain, the grass would grow green again, and people would come to live on the prairie. But how could he make it rain?

The Indians made a great noise, shaking rattles
and beating drums, whenever they wanted to
attract the rain. It nearly always worked. Febold
had no rattle and no drum. He'd have to think of
something else. Frogs, of course, made a big racket
with their croaking.

The problem was solved. Febold Feboldson
gathered together all the frogs from the dried-up
Dismal River. They refused to croak at first. He
had forgotten that they croak only when it is
raining. But this didn't stop him. He put the frogs
under a spell. Gently he stroked their heads and
murmured into their ears, "It's raining. It's raining. It's raining."

Before long, the frogs believed him. They had
fallen under his spell so completely that they
thought it really was raining. One at a time they
croaked, softly and timidly, then loudly and boldly.
The noise grew and grew.

And then came the miracle. The sky became
gray with clouds. A low roll of thunder sounded
and a wind blew up from nowhere. Splash! A few
drops at a time, then a light shower, and finally
in a cloudburst came the rain. Nebraska was saved!

The Blizzard of '98

Ellis Credle

Hank Huggins sat on the porch of his cabin one cold March day, his feet propped on the rail. He was looking out over the long blue ranges of the Blue Ridge Mountains.

"Cold enough for you, Hank?" asked a neighbor who had stopped to borrow a pint of lamp-oil.

"Why no," said Hank. "My mind was just working back to the blizzard of '98. Folks that didn't see that blizzard haven't got any idea of what cold weather is." Hank settled himself for the following tale.

It came on suddenly. One minute, it was near about as warm as summer. The next, everything was frozen stiff and hanging with icicles a foot long. Some cattle that were a-pasturing out on a hillside right near my cabin piled up on top of one another to get warm. They froze into a pyramid as hard as a rock. But the freakiest thing I ever heard of was what happened to my old lady.

I was across the valley, where you see that cabin with the smoke a-rising from the chimney. A-walking, it's a mighty far piece over there. But, as the crow flies, it's near-within hollering distance. Well, sir, when my wife saw the sky darkening all of a sudden and heard the wind whistling down from the high peaks, it scarified her half out of her wits. She ran into the front yard and yelled across the valley for me to come home.

I was a-standing in the front yard across the way. I saw her come into the yard. I saw her jaws a-working like she was talking. But I never heard a sound. Anyway, one look at the weather told me I'd never get home before the storm broke. I hustled into the house with my neighbor and we slammed the door. Well, sir, just as I told you, it was a blizzard to end all blizzards.

After the worst was over, the sun came out. I set off for home. Everything was coated with ice and a-glittering like crystal. I slid downwards through a glass forest and chipped my way up the other side. Everything you looked at was like an ornament to put on the mantelpiece.

When I got home, the old lady was in a temper. "Why didn't you answer when I called you?" she shouted at me as I came in the door. "Seems you could have said yes or no or something!"

"I didn't hear you say anything," I threw back at her.

"Don't tell me you didn't hear anything!" she cried. "I've been hollering across that valley too many years to think I couldn't make myself heard!"

Well, we talked it back and forth, she claiming

that she hollered for me, I allowing that she never
made a sound. We were still at it hot and heavy
when a queer noise in the air made us stop stock-
still. At first it sounded like an old phonograph
record starting off slow-like. Then it picked up.
And out there in the blue air, between the two
mountains, came a shout, "Hank! You, Hank
Huggi-i-ins! Look at the sky! It's a-going to snow!
You come on home right now before you get
caught away from home!"

It was my old lady's voice—to the life. And she hadn't said a word! We looked at each other, our eyes fairly popping. "They're my very words!" she whispered as though she'd heard a ghost. "They're the very words I hollered when the blizzard was a-blowing down!"

Well, sir, for a minute there, my brains were fairly scattered. I didn't know what to think. Then it came to me.

"Why, of course," I said. "Can't you see what happened? That blizzard was so cold and it came up so suddenly that it froze your words in mid-air. They never got to the other side. Now, with the weather warming up, they've thawed out."

"Well, Hank," said the neighbor, picking up his bottle of lamp oil, and setting off down the path, "I agree with you. The folks that missed that blizzard don't know what cold weather really is!"

It Could
Happen to You

Adventures aren't all hunting treasures;
There are other sorts of pleasures:
Finding shells on sandy beaches,
Wiping dishes, picking peaches,
Going out for family rides:
Adventures all—and fun besides!

—*Dorothy Hall*

Any Old Junk Today?

Carolyn Haywood

Never a week went by without Eddie's bringing home some piece of what Eddie called "valuable property," and his father called "junk."

The family always knew when Eddie had brought home a new treasure. Eddie would always announce at dinner, "I had a very enjoyable day today." When Eddie said this, his father would look at his mother and say, "Uh! Oh!"

After dinner, his father would go down to the basement. There he would find another piece of junk added to Eddie's collection.

"Now, see here, Edward!" said his father one evening. "This junk collecting has reached the limit. I am tired of it. The basement looks like a junk shop, or worse. This thing has got to stop."

Eddie looked very downcast. "But, Pop!" said Eddie. "It's my valuable property."

"Valuable property!" exclaimed his father. "Junk!"

The following Saturday, Rudy and the twins went on a hike with some of the boys in Rudy's class. Eddie wanted to go, too, but they said that he was too little. He felt very bad until his mother said that he could go with her and his father. They were driving out into the country to see if they could buy an old table.

It was a beautiful day. As they drove along the roads, Eddie saw the cows and the horses on the farms. He saw men working in the fields. He read the signs along the road. FRESH EGGS. BROILERS.

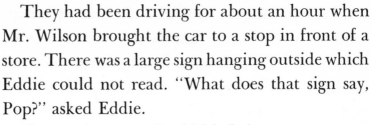

They had been driving for about an hour when Mr. Wilson brought the car to a stop in front of a store. There was a large sign hanging outside which Eddie could not read. "What does that sign say, Pop?" asked Eddie.

"It says ANTIQUES," said his father.

"Are we going to see Aunt Teek?" asked Eddie. "Does she own the store?"

"Not Aunt Teek," said his father. "Antiques. *Antique* means old. It means that the shop sells old things."

"You mean junk?" said Eddie.

"No, indeed!" said his father. "These things are valuable."

Mr. and Mrs. Wilson and Eddie walked up the path to the porch. The porch was full of all kinds of objects. Among them were some huge kettles, some fire screens, and brass and iron andirons. There were long iron forks, and tongs for handling the logs in a fireplace.

"Gee!" said Eddie. "It sure looks like junk."

All the windows were filled with shelves. The shelves were covered with glass vases, cups, plates, pitchers, and sugar bowls. The inside of the store

was stuffed with tables, chairs, chests of drawers, and cabinets full of china.

"Jeepers!" thought Eddie. "I'll bet a fellow could find some very valuable property around here."

While his father and mother were talking to the owner of the shop, Eddie looked over the shelves. He peered into open boxes and barrels. Finally, he went through a doorway into a storeroom. There he came upon a man opening a barrel.

"Hello, son!" said the man. "Can I do something for you?"

"I'm just looking around," said Eddie.

In a moment, Eddie's eyes fell upon something that interested him very much indeed. On a shelf stood an old carriage lamp. It was rusty and covered with dust.

"Do you want to sell that lamp?" Eddie asked the man who was opening the barrel.

The man looked up. "I guess we do."

"How much is it?" asked Eddie.

"Oh, 'bout a quarter," said the man.

Eddie reached into his pocket and pulled out all his money. He had seventy-five cents.

"Okay!" said Eddie, briskly, "I'll take it."

The man took the lamp from the shelf. Just then, Eddie's eye fell upon another interesting object. It looked like a small iron urn with a wheel on each side. It, too, was rusty.

"What is that?" asked Eddie.

"Oh, that?" asked the man, lifting it down. "That's an old-fashioned coffee grinder."

"Those wheels are super!" said Eddie, his eyes very big. "How much is that?"

"Oh, I guess I can let you have that for fifty cents," said the man.

Eddie looked at the coffee grinder. Then he said, "I'll take that, too."

"Want them wrapped?" asked the man.

"Yes, please," replied Eddie. He watched the man put the coffee grinder and lamp into a cardboard box. When he folded over the flaps, they didn't close because the end of the lamp was too long. The man tied a piece of cord over the top to hold the flaps down, but the end of the lamp still showed.

"I guess that will do," he said.

"Oh, sure!" replied Eddie, as he handed over his seventy-five cents. "That will do."

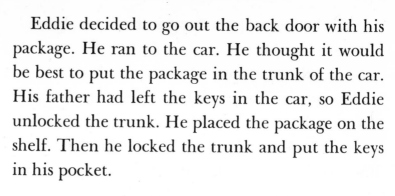

Eddie decided to go out the back door with his package. He ran to the car. He thought it would be best to put the package in the trunk of the car. His father had left the keys in the car, so Eddie unlocked the trunk. He placed the package on the shelf. Then he locked the trunk and put the keys in his pocket.

Some Valuable Property

Eddie sauntered back to the front porch. He was looking at a broken lock when his father and mother came out.

"Look, Pop," said Eddie. "This is a swell lock."

"It's a piece of junk," said Mr. Wilson. "No more junk is going into our house, Eddie. Put it down."

Eddie put the lock down and walked to the car with his father and mother. "You left the keys in the car, Pop," said Eddie, handing over the keys.

"Oh, thanks, Eddie," said his father. They all climbed into the car. Eddie sat between his father and mother.

For some time they drove in silence. Then Eddie said, "Well, I had a very enjoyable time."

Mr. and Mrs. Wilson immediately looked down at Eddie. He looked up at them with a sweet smile.

Mr. Wilson put on the brakes and stopped the car. He looked around on the back seat of the car and on the floor. There was nothing there.

"What did you say, Eddie?" his father asked.

Eddie looked up. "I just said I've had a very enjoyable time."

Mr. Wilson took the keys from the car. He walked around and opened the trunk. There was Eddie's package.

Eddie said, "Please, Pop, it isn't junk. It's swell stuff."

"Eddie, when I said, 'No more junk,' I meant it." To Eddie's amazement, his father placed the package in a ditch beside the road.

As Mr. Wilson leaned over, he saw the end of the lamp sticking out of the top of the box. He pulled off the cord and lifted out the lamp.

"Say!" he cried. "Why, this is a carriage lamp. I have been wanting one of these for a long time. I want it to go on the post at the front gate. Why, this is a beautiful carriage lamp. It just needs to be refinished. Well, now!"

"But I bought it, Pop," said Eddie. "I paid for it."

"Well, I'll give you a dollar for it, Eddie," said his father. "How is that?"

"Okay!" said Eddie.

Mrs. Wilson joined Eddie and his father.

"Look, Mother!" Mr. Wilson cried. "Look at this fine carriage lamp. This is mine."

Mrs. Wilson was busy looking into the box. "Why, look at this old coffee grinder!" she cried. "Oh, this is mine! These old coffee grinders make the most beautiful lamps you ever saw! With a coat of red paint, this will be perfect."

"But I bought it, Mamma," said Eddie. "I paid for it."

"Oh, well. I'll give you a dollar for it," said his mother. "Is a dollar all right?"

"Ah, Mamma!" said Eddie. "I like that coffee grinder. I like it a lot."

"Well, I'll give you two dollars for it," said his mother. "That's a lot of money, Eddie."

"Okay!" said Eddie.

The three went back to the car. Mr. Wilson went first, carrying his carriage lamp. Then Mrs. Wilson, carrying her coffee grinder. Little Eddie brought up the rear, with three dollars in his small fist.

"By the way, Eddie," Mr. Wilson said, "How much did you pay for that lamp?"

"A quarter," said Eddie.

"And how much did you pay for the coffee grinder?" asked his father.

"Fifty cents," Eddie replied.

"Not bad!" said his father, looking at his mother.

"You know, Pop!" said Eddie. "I've been thinking. Do you know what I'm going to be when I grow up?"

"No," replied Mr. Wilson. "What are you going to be?"

"I'm going to be a junk man," said Eddie. "That's a good way to get rich."

The Fish Money

Mildred Lawrence

*Cissie, an orphan, had come in the fall
to live with her Uncle Eben and Mrs.
Halloran, his housekeeper. Uncle
Eben had a peach farm on Peachtree
Island. Now the winter was here.*

"Warmer or colder or just the same?" wondered
Cissie all day long. On the whole, she thought it
seemed colder, which might be good or might be
bad. "I could tell so much better if only I knew
what he wants this weather for!"

When the bus stopped in front of Uncle Eben's house after school, Cissie leaped out almost before the wheels stopped rolling.

"Your Uncle Eben's waiting for you," called Mrs. Halloran from the kitchen. "Put on those heavy galoshes and an extra sweater, because you'll need them."

Uncle Eben had the car attached to a little house on skis, just like one Cissie had seen going by on the road the night before.

"Let's go," said Uncle Eben. "We'll have little enough time as it is."

Cissie hopped into the car. Uncle Eben started up the road, with the little house sliding crazily along behind.

"Where are we going?" asked Cissie when she couldn't stand it any longer.

"Fishing," said Uncle Eben.

"You're just teasing," said Cissie. "How could we go fishing in this weather? And what's the little house for?"

"Curiosity killed a cat," said Uncle Eben. "Wait and see."

He drove along the lake and back to the place

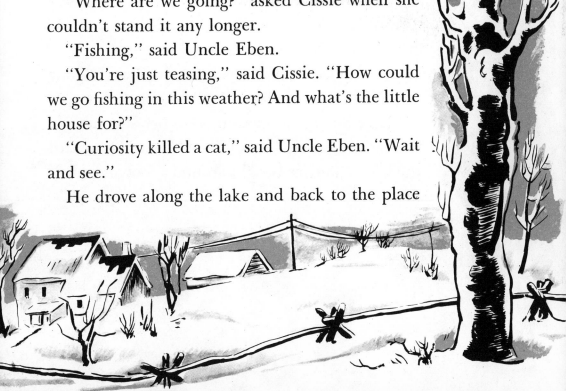

where Cissie had come off the boat last fall. It all looked very strange now, with nothing left of the merry-go-round but an open space.

Only the big general store was open. Several cars were parked in front of it and people were rushing in and out. The women came out carrying lumpy sacks of groceries. The men had big bags of chicken feed on their shoulders.

"It's like two different places," said Cissie. "One place in the summer and another in winter."

"That's right," said Uncle Eben, stopping the car at the place where the water would have begun if it hadn't all turned to ice. He unhitched the little house from the car. "Now, then, if you'll just help me pull, we'll get going."

Cissie noticed then that the little house was drawn by a rope, just like a sled. She and Uncle Eben took hold and started out.

"On the ice?" asked Cissie. She had never gone walking on a lake before. "Will it hold all this up?"

"How do you suppose those other shanties got out there?" Uncle Eben jerked his thumb toward the lake. "The ice is right around a foot-and-a-half thick now."

For the first time, Cissie noticed that there were dozens of little shanties like Uncle Eben's scattered along the ice not far from shore.

"It looks like a toy village," she said.

It wasn't long before Uncle Eben found a place that suited him. "This is just right," he said. "We'll unlock our front door and get busy."

He took the padlock off the door of the shanty and they stepped in. It was a very nice little house, Cissie thought. It was about five feet square, with a bench along each side. Higher up was a shelf full of all kinds of strange things. A round hole had been cut in the floor. Uncle Eben took an ice ax from the shelf and hacked a hole in the ice directly under the hole in the floor.

"Now, then," he said. "We're ready to begin."

He unrolled four fishlines, attached hooks and sinkers to them, and tied them to nails in the side of the shanty. Then, reaching into the bait can, he put bait on every hook.

"All right, now, let's see what you can catch." He dropped the lines into the hole in the ice. "You watch those lines while I get this heater going."

"If I were a fish, I wouldn't come out in this cold weather," said Cissie. She still felt very doubtful about the whole thing.

"If you were a hungry fish," said Uncle Eben, "you'd come out in any kind of weather." He lit the heater and stood it in one corner of the shanty. "Hey! Something's pulling your line!"

Callers from the Deep

Something was, but Cissie never found out *what* it was. In a minute the line went slack. When Cissie finished pulling it in, the bait was gone.

"Oh, dear!" she wailed. "I just know it would have been a big one!"

"Life is full of sorrow," said Uncle Eben solemnly. He put more bait on the hook. "Hey! Haul in that one to the left."

This time Cissie actually got a fish—a plump perch which she thought was the largest, handsomest fish she had ever seen. Uncle Eben took it off the hook and tossed it into a bushel basket.

"Now, then," he said, "we're off to a good start. It's just a matter of breaking the ice."

Cissie giggled. "It certainly is," she said.

"Look here," said Uncle Eben. "That second line of yours has been jerking for five minutes. That fish probably thinks he has to ring the doorbell before you'll pull him in!"

It turned out to be a very good day for fishing. Uncle Eben and Cissie filled one bushel basket with fish and started to fill the next.

"I always thought bushel baskets were to hold fruit," said Cissie. "But on Peachtree Island they're for fish and apple peelings and sliced apples and Mrs. Halloran's washing and—"

"Yes," said Uncle Eben. "But just wait until summer. Then you'll see them used for fruit—lots of it. Haul in! You've got another bite!"

"What'll we do with all these fish?" asked Cissie. "We'll be eating fish for a month."

Outside, a horn sounded. A voice said, "Any fish

for Hennessy?'' Drawn up in front of the shanty was a little old truck with a sign painted on the side—HENNESSY'S FISH MARKET.

"Sure have,'' said Uncle Eben. "Best fish you ever saw, too.''

"That's what they all say,'' said the big, red-faced man in the truck. "And it wouldn't be me that'd be saying they were wrong. Let's see 'em!''

Uncle Eben brought out the baskets. Mr. Hennessy weighed them on his scales.

"Sixty pounds and a mite over,'' he said, reaching for his wallet.

Cissie tugged at Uncle Eben's sleeve.

"We haven't saved any for supper,'' she said.

"My, oh, my, I completely forgot Mrs. Halloran,'' said Uncle Eben. "Maybe—hey, that center line is jerking! Yank it up and see what we've got.''

It was another fish, nice and fat.

"Lucky for us,'' said Uncle Eben to Mr. Hennessy. "Take all the rest.''

Mr. Hennessy counted out some money and drove on to the next shanty, where he tooted his horn again.

Uncle Eben handed Cissie six crisp dollar bills. "Your share of the swag," he said.

Cissie's eyes opened wide. "But you furnished the bait and the shanty and the lines."

"But you helped pull the shanty out here, and also you caught the first fish, which is very, very important."

Cissie hugged Uncle Eben. "Thank you ever and ever so much," she said.

"How'll you spend it?" asked Uncle Eben.

"That's a secret," said Cissie. She had been worrying about how to buy Christmas presents for Uncle Eben and Mrs. Halloran.

"We'd better get going," said Uncle Eben, pulling in another fish. "The fishing's good, but if we're late for supper, Mrs. Halloran'll have our heads."

Whopper

Nan Gilbert

Whopper Mason was trotting home as fast as his two short legs could carry him. A thin trickle of blood dropped from his nose.

"Boy, oh, boy," he chanted aloud to himself, "was that a fight!" He doubled up his fists and pretended to down an enemy. "Boy, oh, boy, I certainly had him on the run!"

A boy stood suddenly in his path, a bigger boy than Whopper. "Hi, Whopper," he said. "Where'd you get the nose?"

Whopper kept on poking his fists at thin air. "Fighting," he answered excitedly. "Boy, was that a fight! First I sock him, and then he socks me, and then I sock him, and then . . ."

"Who?" said the big boy.

"Willie Taylor. And then he socks me, and . . ."

"Willie Taylor isn't allowed to fight. His mother won't like it a bit when I tell her."

Some of the punch went out of Whopper then. His fists poked feebly, and then fell to his sides. He wiped at his nose with his handkerchief.

"Oh," he said. "Isn't he? Aw, shucks," he admitted. "He wasn't really fighting, Jess. I just took a poke at him, and . . . and . . ."

"And what?" said Jess.

"And I swung so hard I fell down," Whopper confessed. "And that's what happened to my nose."

"That's what I thought," Jess said. "Whopper Mason, when are you going to quit making up those big stories? If you'd kept on with this one, you'd have got Willie in trouble."

Whopper kicked at the dirt with his toe. "Well, I guess I'm *trying*, Jess," he said. "Only sometimes I forget."

He went on his way, very depressed. Telling big stories, Jess called it. Ex-ag-ger-ating, his parents said. But to Whopper, it was only making dull things exciting. Nevertheless, he was going to stop it, just as he'd promised Jess.

He scattered his jacks on the front walk at home. He was going to try the whole game—from "one jack" to "jack around the world"—and see if he could go through without missing. He never had yet. The little boy next door came over to watch, but Whopper sent him home again for fear he'd get in the way.

Whopper had got to "jack in the sty" without a single miss, when he saw the man.

He was a big man, at least to Whopper's eyes, with a mustache and a cane. He was talking to the little boy next door. Whopper went back to his jacks, but he did notice the little boy walking away with the man presently.

Whopper reached "jack around the world," and carefully went through its moves. Then he whooped excitedly.

"I made it!" he yelled. "I got through the whole game! Yippee!"

A hand was shaking his shoulder. It was the mother of the little boy next door. "Whopper," she was asking anxiously, "have you seen Petie?"

"Oh, sure," Whopper answered. "A man took him away."

Petie's mother looked still more anxious. "A man?" she cried. "What did he look like?"

Whopper felt the pleasant glow of creation spreading within him. "Oh, an enormous man," he recited happily. "Just *enormous!* Like the fellows Popeye knocks out. And his face was all hairy . . . big black beard 'n everything. And he had a great big stick in his hand. . . ."

Petie's mother was looking scared. "Oh, my goodness," she said over and over, running to her house. "Oh, my goodness!"

Whopper felt quite pleased with himself. He went in for a drink. That really had been an exciting story. But then, Whopper's heart sank. Hadn't that been ex-ag-ger-ating? Anyway, a little? He thought of Jess and squirmed.

"Shucks," muttered Whopper. "Oh, shucks."

He diddled a little longer over his drink, but his way was plain before him. Slowly, slowly, he went across the lawn to Petie's home. The yard was filled with people, all talking loudly. But Whopper hardly saw them. He singled out Petie's mother.

Whopper Keeps a Promise

"Say," he said, feeling dreadfully uncomfortable. "Say, that fellow that walked away with Petie . . . he wasn't so big, not so awfully big." A silence fell on the group of people. Still Whopper didn't notice. He was too busy trying to describe the stranger exactly.

"And he didn't have a beard," he went on, "just a little teeny black mustache. And he carried a cane, not a stick."

Petie's mother dropped limply down on the porch steps. "Why, that was John," she cried, "Petie's Uncle John. And I thought Petie'd been kidnapped!" She whirled suddenly on Whopper. "Whopper Mason!" she began severely.

Fifteen minutes later, Whopper was still trying to forget what she and everybody else had said. Shucks, a body'd think they'd rather Petie'd been kidnapped than have been scared for nothing. A fine lot of good it did a person to tell the truth. Though, he admitted honestly, if he'd told the exact truth *first,* nobody would have been scared.

Whopper had two pennies in his pocket, and he was going to spend them. He felt the need of a couple of good suckers. Orange, he thought.

"Rrrruff!" something said at his heels. Whopper jumped. A little black Scotty had whirled out of the bushes, and was worrying his shoes.

"Whoa!" Whopper said, moving ahead at a fast clip. A backward look told him the Scotty wasn't following. His dragging leash seemed tangled in the bushes. But Whopper wasn't taking any chances on its getting *un*tangled. He kept on running all the way to the drugstore.

"Whew!" he gasped, bursting in the door. "Was I ever scared!"

A man phoning at the far end of the counter frowned at him. Whopper lowered his voice politely, but his excitement rose high.

"A big dog chased me!" he told the drugstore man importantly. "A great, big barking dog. Must have been a St. Bernard or something!"

"St. Bernards are friendly," the drugstore man said. "Could it have been a police dog?"

"Must have been," Whopper cried happily.

"Chased me for blocks. I tried to climb a tree, and it pulled me down, and I just barely got over a fence. . . ."

His high spirits suddenly faded. He was remembering Jess. Slowly, his shoulders sagged.

"Naw," he admitted. "Wasn't a police dog." The scene at Petie's house came back to him. Maybe he'd just not explain things any further. But Jess wouldn't like that.

Reluctantly, Whopper added, "Was a little dog . . . little black fellow. Didn't chase me, either."

Low as his voice had been, the man at the phone had heard him. He slammed down the receiver and came rushing. "What's that you said?" he cried. "What kind of a dog?"

Whopper backed away from him. What kind of trouble was coming now? Maybe he'd better go back to the police dog story. But the thought of Jess held him. He'd just have to stick to the truth.

"Yep," he muttered. "Just a wee little black dog it was. And its leash was tangled in the bushes so it couldn't chase me if it wanted to."

"What bushes?" the man asked excitedly. "Show me!"

MENUS

More and more worried, Whopper led the way. The Scotty was still there, barking louder and louder as it tried to free itself.

"Dennis!" the man with Whopper yelled. "You little rascal!" He grabbed up the dog into his arms, freeing the leash with one hand.

"Little boy," he told Whopper, "you've done me a mighty good turn. Dennis here ran away today. We've been scouring the town for him. I was just phoning in a 'Lost and Found' ad, offering a reward. So I guess now you've got that coming, haven't you?"

Whopper couldn't answer. His eyes were bulging out with excitement. He closed his hand over the bill the man slipped into it, and watched the stranger and his dog disappear down the block.

"Boy!" he said. He looked wide-eyed at the five-dollar bill he was holding. "Boy, now I've got something to tell that doesn't *need* ex-ag-ger-ating!"

Judy Grows Up

Sally Scott

It was a queer summer for Judy. Her mother spent most of the time taking care of Judy's baby brother, Buzzie. Judy felt that babies sort of spoiled things.

"We could go down to the river," Laura suggested. Mary Anne shook her head and sat down with a thump.

"It's too far," she said. "I'm *hot!*" Judy flopped down on the grass beside them. It was nice to be with Laura and Mary Anne. These days, the farther she got from home the better she felt.

"I wonder where Lou Mae is this summer?" she asked. "She hasn't been to the park once."

"Say, that's right!" Laura sat up.

"I saw her mother in the ten-cent store last week," Mary Anne added. "They haven't moved."

They were all sitting up now. Just thinking of Lou Mae made them feel livelier. Lou Mae was small and skinny. Her teeth stuck out in front and her clothes were simply awful. But when it came to playing, Lou Mae was the most fun of anybody they knew. Nobody was ever bored when Lou Mae was around. And suddenly Judy said, "Let's go and see her!"

Where Lou Mae lived there were no sidewalks. The yards went right down to the street and were full of garbage cans and washing on the line. But the alley by Lou Mae's house was empty and quiet. An old cat sat on the porch beside the tin cans of geraniums. Suddenly, the screen door flew back and there was Lou Mae herself. She had a big apron around her middle and a broom in her hand —just as bouncy as ever, her pigtails flying as she swished the dirt out of the door.

When she saw them, she waved the broom over her head.

"Hey, kids!" she shouted, beaming all over. "Hey! It's swell to see you. Come on in! How are you? Been swimming much?"

"We're all right," Laura answered. "Where've

you been all summer anyway? We haven't seen you for ages."

Lou Mae held the screen door open for them as they went in. "I've been working!" she told them proudly. "I can't come out and play until Mom gets through with her job."

"Working?" the girls stared. Lou Mae wasn't any older than they were.

Lou Mae snatched a pile of dirty clothes off the couch. "Sit down, won't you? Mom had a chance to wash dishes in the restaurant, so I'm minding the baby for her."

All three of them looked across the room at the old baby carriage in the corner. A fat baby girl sat beaming at them. Lou Mae darted across the room to her.

"Isn't she sweet?" Lou Mae demanded. "She's Lou Mae's own precious, aren't you, lover? Look at her dimples!" The baby giggled and ducked her head as Lou Mae tickled her under her chin.

"See all the girls come to see you? Show them how you play hide and seek. Come on, go boo!"

And sure enough, the baby put her fat, dimpled hands over her face a minute, and said "Boo," in

a whisper as she pushed them away. Then she burst into giggles and hid her face in Lou Mae's skirt.

"Here, Baby, here's your lamb. Lou Mae's got to fix the potatoes. Be a good girl now." And Lou Mae came back to the table and picked up the paring knife, just like a grownup. "Come on and tell me some news," she said to the girls. "What's been going on?"

Laura and Mary Anne started talking, but Judy didn't listen much. She felt queer. Lou Mae talked just the way Mother did. And she looked so cheerful! Judy stared at the baby's round, sticky face across the room, and the baby giggled and hid behind her woolly lamb. Babies might be cute when they got big enough to learn tricks, Judy thought.

Lou Mae stopped what she was saying to Laura.

"She's awfully shy," she told Judy proudly. "But I've taught her to smile at people now."

Just like Mother! Judy was still wondering, when they said goodbye, why it made her feel so funny.

Judy Takes a Hand

Judy felt so glad to get home she didn't even mind that Mother didn't stop to hug her. She sat at the kitchen table thinking how nice and clean and shining her kitchen looked after Lou Mae's. She listened to Mother talk about her shopping and when Daddy would come home, and how would it be if they had biscuits for supper?

"Oh, *yes,* Mother! Let's!" said Judy.

But Mother had stopped, and was staring at the sink.

"Heavens, no! I won't have time!" she said. "I forgot about the baby's bottles!"

Always! Always Buzzie spoiled everything! But home felt so good this time it was hard to get cross. Judy said, without even thinking about it, "Please let's have biscuits, Mother! Wouldn't you have time if I did the bottles?"

Mother stopped halfway to the sink. "Would you, Judy?" She looked at the bottles. "Could you?"

"I've washed glasses without breaking them," Judy reminded her. "Or do you have to do something extra special for babies' things?"

She thought of Lou Mae bustling around her kitchen. Something made her get up and go over to the sink instead of waiting for Mother to decide.

"Come on, Mother! They can't be *that* special."

Mother laughed a little. "You sound like Daddy," she said. "No, they're just like glasses, really. Only you have to rinse them more. Here, I'll show you."

And really, they were more fun than glasses even, Judy thought, as she sat by the sink sozzling the suds up and down with the bottle washer. That

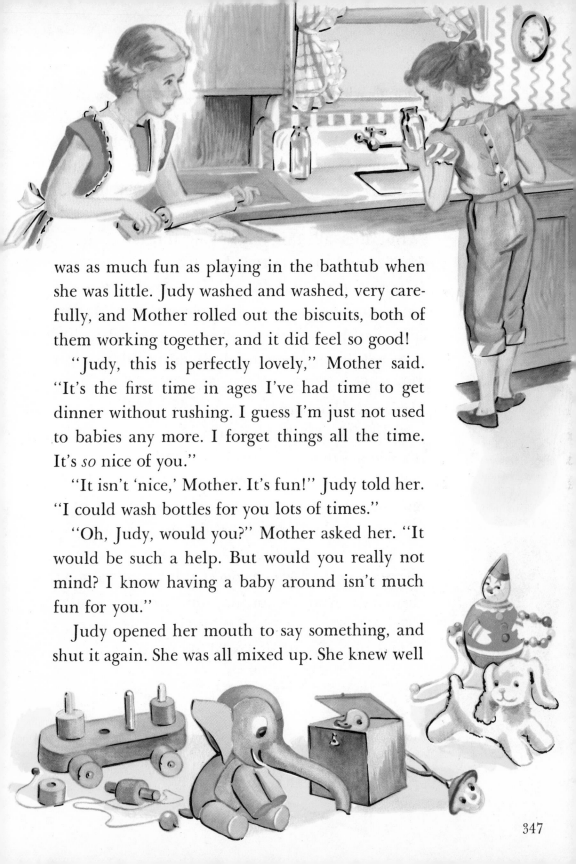

was as much fun as playing in the bathtub when she was little. Judy washed and washed, very carefully, and Mother rolled out the biscuits, both of them working together, and it did feel so good!

"Judy, this is perfectly lovely," Mother said. "It's the first time in ages I've had time to get dinner without rushing. I guess I'm just not used to babies any more. I forget things all the time. It's *so* nice of you."

"It isn't 'nice,' Mother. It's fun!" Judy told her. "I could wash bottles for you lots of times."

"Oh, Judy, would you?" Mother asked her. "It would be such a help. But would you really not mind? I know having a baby around isn't much fun for you."

Judy opened her mouth to say something, and shut it again. She was all mixed up. She knew well enough what Mother was talking about—how cross she got lots of times when Mother asked her to do something special on account of Buzzie. And sure enough, just talking about him brought back the same feeling, dark and queer and different, like stamping her foot and slamming doors.

But after all, this was having fun too, helping Mother and visiting together like two grownups. It wasn't a bit like the old days when there was only Judy, and she sat at the table watching Mother cook, and having pieces of dough popped in her mouth if she was a good girl. But although this was different, it was nice, too. She wanted to make Mother understand.

"I like *this* kind of helping, Mother. *With* you. It's when I'm all by myself it's no fun."

And now it was Mother who first opened her mouth and then shut it again. She looked at Judy a minute without saying anything. Then she put the biscuit pan on the table and said in a rather surprised voice, "You know, I think that's a good idea, Judy. And it's not just you. I think it would be more fun for me, too. Let's do it this way more."

And that was all they said about it.

Skipping Along Alone

Oh, how I love to skip alone
    Along the beach in moisty weather;
The whole world seems my very own,
Each fluted shell and glistening stone,
    Each wave that twirls a silver feather.

I skip along so brave and big
    Behind the sand-birds gray and tiny,
I love to see their quick feet jig,
Each leaves a mark, neat as a twig,
    Stamped in the sand so clear and shiny.

And fine and faint as drops of spray
    I hear their little voices calling,
"Sweet, sweet! Sweet, sweet!" I hear them say—
I love to skip alone and play
    Along the sand when mist is falling.

                —*Winifred Welles*

The Animal Store

If I had a hundred dollars to spend,
  Or maybe a little more,
I'd hurry as fast as my legs would go
  Straight to the animal store.

I wouldn't say, "How much for this or that?"—
  "What kind of a dog is he?"
I'd buy as many as rolled an eye,
  Or wagged a tail at me!

I'd take the hound with the drooping ears
  That sits by himself alone;
Cockers and Cairns and wobbly pups
  For to be my very own.

I might buy a parrot all red and green,
  And the monkey I saw before,
If I had a hundred dollars to spend,
  Or maybe a little more.

—*Rachel Field*

City Rain

Rain in the city!
    I love to see it fall
Slantwise where the buildings crowd
    Red brick and all.
Streets of shiny wetness
    Where the taxis go,
With people and umbrellas all
    Bobbing to and fro.

Rain in the city!
    I love to hear it drip
When I am cosy in my room
    Snug as any ship,
With toys spread on the table,
    With a picture book or two,
And the rain like a rumbling tune that sings
    Through everything I do.

—*Rachel Field*

351

There Was a Time

There was a time when in our land,
    Dark and green and still,
The forests stretched as thick as fur
    From hill to hill to hill.
A sea of leaves drank down the rain
    And twinkled in the breeze,
When half of all America
    Was trees and trees and trees.

—*Dorothy Hall*

The *Mayflower* Spaniel

Catherine Coblentz

When the first settlers came to the New World, they brought animals with them, some for food, and some for protection and companionship. The two dogs in this story came to Plymouth with the Pilgrims in 1620 and were important enough to be mentioned in the records of two Pilgrim leaders, William Bradford and Edward Winslow.

The English Mastiff and the little Dutch Spaniel were lying in the shadow of one of the linden trees that bordered the streets of Leyden. Because they were about to depart on a long journey across the sea to the New World, they were both excited. Yet many minutes had passed since either of the dogs had said a word.

The Mastiff lay quietly, her tongue lolling from her mouth, but the little Spaniel kept jumping up every few minutes. He would race down the street, giving short, excited yelps.

From ANIMAL PIONEERS by Catherine Coblentz. Published 1936 by Little, Brown & Company. Reprinted by permission of the author's estate

"For goodness' sakes," growled the Mastiff finally, "why *don't* you be quiet? You heard my master say we should not start this long voyage right away."

"Yes, yes, I know," barked the Spaniel, "but I must get in condition. I shall do a lot of hunting in America. There are lions there, I've heard the Pilgrims say. I am getting in practice to hunt them."

The Mastiff looked at her small companion and sniffed. "Aren't you anxious to hunt lions?" questioned the Spaniel.

"I shall serve my master in whatever way is best. Usually I have found this is done by guarding the house door. Besides, the Pilgrims only said there *might* be lions there. They are not certain." And the Mastiff laid her head on her paw and slept.

But the Spaniel wrinkled his nose at his companion's words, and continued to rush wildly about the streets of Leyden until the day came for the sailing of the two dogs with their Pilgrim masters to England.

From England, at last, the two dogs departed on the *Mayflower* for America. There could be no

chasing of imaginary lions on that ship, for it was too crowded. All the Spaniel could do was lie quietly and think of all the mighty things he was going to accomplish. Guard the house indeed! He would do much braver things than that.

However, when after many weeks the *Mayflower* came to anchor at Plymouth Harbor, the Spaniel's legs were strangely wobbly, so that for a time he stayed quietly beside the Mastiff and watched the first house in Plymouth being built.

He grew tired of this as the days passed and his legs steadied beneath him. "Come, let us be after lions," he urged the Mastiff. But she only shook one ear and kept her large eyes fastened on her master as he helped saw logs and fasten the frame together with wooden pins.

"Oh, dear, I shall *never* get any hunting done at this rate," thought the Spaniel.

Finally the walls of the house were finished. Peter Browne and John Goodman and two other men were gathering grass with which to thatch the roof. When lunch time came and the men paused to eat, the Spaniel began running off a little to one side and yelping sharply.

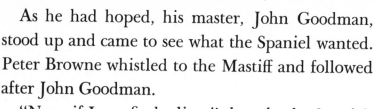

As he had hoped, his master, John Goodman, stood up and came to see what the Spaniel wanted. Peter Browne whistled to the Mastiff and followed after John Goodman.

"Now, if I can find a lion," thought the Spaniel, "we'll be hunting at last."

An Adventure in the Woods

As the four of them approached a pond, his wish seemed to be granted. There was a flash of brown across his path. With one look behind to be certain that the Mastiff followed, the Spaniel took after it.

His long practice in running along the streets of Leyden didn't seem to help him much, for the Mastiff moved even more swiftly than he. But the animal they were chasing ran faster than either dog, and they lost its scent when it splashed through the waters of a brook. So the two dogs went back to their masters, who were crashing through the woods after them.

"We'll get the next lion, I'm sure," declared the Spaniel. "I shall run faster next time."

"You didn't think *that* was a lion, did you?" gasped the Mastiff. "That was a deer. We have many in England."

"Oh!" said the Spaniel.

But both dogs soon had something serious to worry them. Hunting in a strange land was one thing. Finding the way back home was another.

"Take us home," ordered John Goodman. The Spaniel looked all about him. Then he dropped his tail, and turned hopefully toward the Mastiff. *Her* eyes grew sad when, after running about in a large circle, she realized that she did not know the way either.

The sun sank, the air turned cold. The Spaniel shivered and crept close to his master's side. It snowed, and darkness closed on men and dogs lost in the strange wood in a strange land.

The silence was broken by a terrible shriek. The little Spaniel's heart leaped to his mouth and he almost whimpered.

"What was that?" he asked the Mastiff.

"Lions, maybe," she answered grimly, standing in front of Peter Browne, ready to leap on any animal that should come at her master from the darkness.

The night passed slowly for the cold and hungry men and dogs. But whenever the shrieks sounded, all forgot their discomfort in fear. Sometimes these noises seemed far off. At other times they seemed to be answered from the forest close at hand.

"I didn't know lions sounded as terrible as that," thought the Spaniel. "I wish John Goodman would pick me up in his arms." He whined a little, and his master did that very thing.

But the Mastiff stood erect, every now and then pulling at her chain. As long as danger threatened, she would do her best to protect her master.

It seemed as though that night would never end. But at last the morning light began to filter through the trees, and the fearful sounds were farther away. Then they were heard no more. Men and dogs began searching again for the place where the first house of Plymouth had just been built.

Those hours of searching were such long hours. At last, when it seemed to the Spaniel that he

could not lift one tired and bleeding paw after another, he heard the Mastiff bark sharply.

She had insisted on climbing a steep hill, and Peter Browne had followed her. After her bark came Peter Browne's shout: "She's done it! She's led us home!"

The Spaniel was glad. "The Mastiff has lived longer than I, and she certainly is wiser," he thought.

Work for a Spaniel

That evening as the two of them lay side by side in front of a roaring fire on the hearth of the new house, the Spaniel tried to tell the Mastiff how he felt. "I really am ashamed of myself," he admitted.

But the Mastiff turned the words aside. "You wouldn't have been so afraid if the animals had really come," she declared. "Strange noises are always frightening. When you can see what causes them, you are not usually so afraid."

The Spaniel was a little comforted. But still he couldn't sleep very well. Whenever he remembered those awful shrieks he would waken with a start.

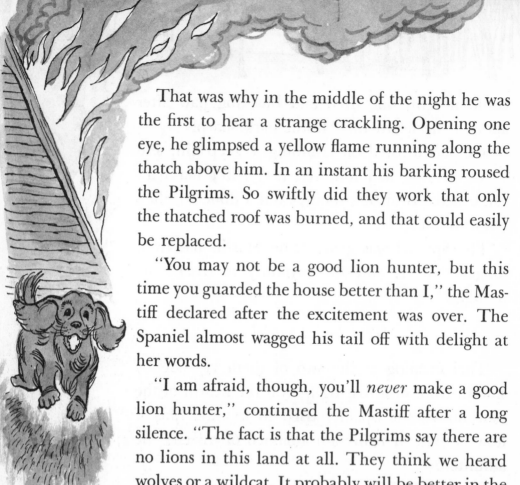

That was why in the middle of the night he was the first to hear a strange crackling. Opening one eye, he glimpsed a yellow flame running along the thatch above him. In an instant his barking roused the Pilgrims. So swiftly did they work that only the thatched roof was burned, and that could easily be replaced.

"You may not be a good lion hunter, but this time you guarded the house better than I," the Mastiff declared after the excitement was over. The Spaniel almost wagged his tail off with delight at her words.

"I am afraid, though, you'll *never* make a good lion hunter," continued the Mastiff after a long silence. "The fact is that the Pilgrims say there are no lions in this land at all. They think we heard wolves or a wildcat. It probably will be better in the future if, instead of hunting, you just help guard the house."

"I'll do my best," agreed the Spaniel. Then the two dogs curled up and slept once more, while a few snowflakes drifted in through the open roof upon them.

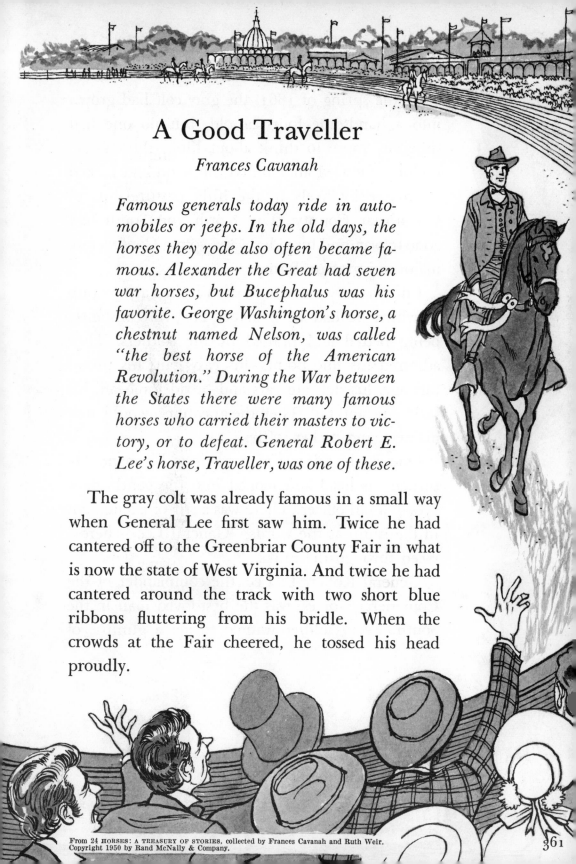

A Good Traveller

Frances Cavanah

*Famous generals today ride in auto-
mobiles or jeeps. In the old days, the
horses they rode also often became famous. Alexander the Great had seven
war horses, but Bucephalus was his
favorite. George Washington's horse, a
chestnut named Nelson, was called
"the best horse of the American
Revolution." During the War between
the States there were many famous
horses who carried their masters to victory, or to defeat. General Robert E.
Lee's horse, Traveller, was one of these.*

The gray colt was already famous in a small way
when General Lee first saw him. Twice he had
cantered off to the Greenbriar County Fair in what
is now the state of West Virginia. And twice he had
cantered around the track with two short blue
ribbons fluttering from his bridle. When the
crowds at the Fair cheered, he tossed his head
proudly.

From 24 HORSES: A TREASURY OF STORIES, collected by Frances Cavanah and Ruth Weir.
Copyright 1950 by Rand McNally & Company.

By the spring of 1861, the gray colt had grown into a handsome four-year-old, but no one had time any more to think about blue ribbons. He no longer grazed and sniffed the wind and kicked up his frisky heels in the hilly pasturelands of Greenbriar County. The North and South had gone to war, and his rider was a young Confederate major in a gray uniform.

Life was very pleasant in the Virginia army camp to which he had been taken. He was constantly being petted and praised by the soldiers. They admired his fine points—his easy gait, his proud carriage, his delicate ears and broad forehead, his full mane and tail. Then the gray horse would arch his neck and nicker softly.

One day he felt a strange hand on his mane. He turned his head and looked into the gentle dark eyes of a tall officer. There was a stir of excitement in the camp as the words, "General Lee is here," raced through the ranks.

General Robert E. Lee, the commander of the Confederate forces, was the best-loved man in the South. Every soldier wanted to get a glimpse of

him as he stood talking to the officer who owned the gray horse.

"Major," said General Lee, "I shall need that horse before the war is over." The handsome gray nuzzled the tall man's shoulder. The General smiled as he stroked the soft gray nose.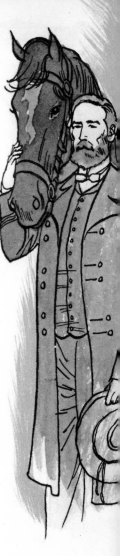

Sometimes it happens that way between a man and a horse. It was love at first sight between the General and the horse from Greenbriar County. Whenever the General visited the camp, the gray horse would quiver with excitement at the touch of the gentle hand on his muzzle.

Several months passed before they saw each other again. The next time they met, it was in South Carolina. The horse had a new rider now, who wanted to present him as a gift to the beloved commander. General Lee refused the gift, but arranged to buy the animal which had attracted him so much.

"He is a good traveller," the General said, after he had ridden him a few times. The name stuck, and Traveller accompanied the army back to Virginia. He arched his proud neck as though he

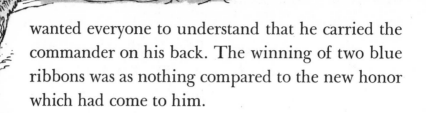

wanted everyone to understand that he carried the commander on his back. The winning of two blue ribbons was as nothing compared to the new honor which had come to him.

Traveller at War

At first Traveller was one of several horses which the General rode. But as one hard month followed another, soldiers in gray and in blue met in battle after battle. They fought and fell back and rushed forward to fight again. General Lee's other horses could not stand up under the strain.

But Traveller never faltered, no matter how long and difficult the march. In the fiercest battle, he did not bolt. But once, at least, he saved his master's life by becoming frightened at the bursting of a shell close by. He suddenly reared, and a shot passed under his girth, just missing the stirrup. Had Traveller been standing on the ground at that instant, his master might have been killed.

Usually, however, Traveller seemed as calm as his rider. The sight of the high-stepping gray horse carrying the General never failed to inspire the men. "Here comes Marse Robert on good old Traveller," they would say as commander and horse passed through the lines. Traveller would acknowledge the cheers by a toss of his graceful neck, and the men would laugh and cheer again.

The sight of the prancing horse inspired them even in battle. Once, when the Confederates were charging Fort Harrison, they fell back before heavy gunfire. The fort was an important one, and the commander urged them to try to storm it a second time. Once more a determined gray line surged forward. Once more it fell back.

Then General Lee rode up on Traveller, his dark eyes gleaming. He leaned forward in the saddle and urged them on with a wave of his sword.

"Try it again!" he shouted. "Try it again!"

"Even Traveller caught the spirit of his master," said one young soldier afterward. "He pranced and cavorted while the General was urging his men to make one more effort to take the fort."

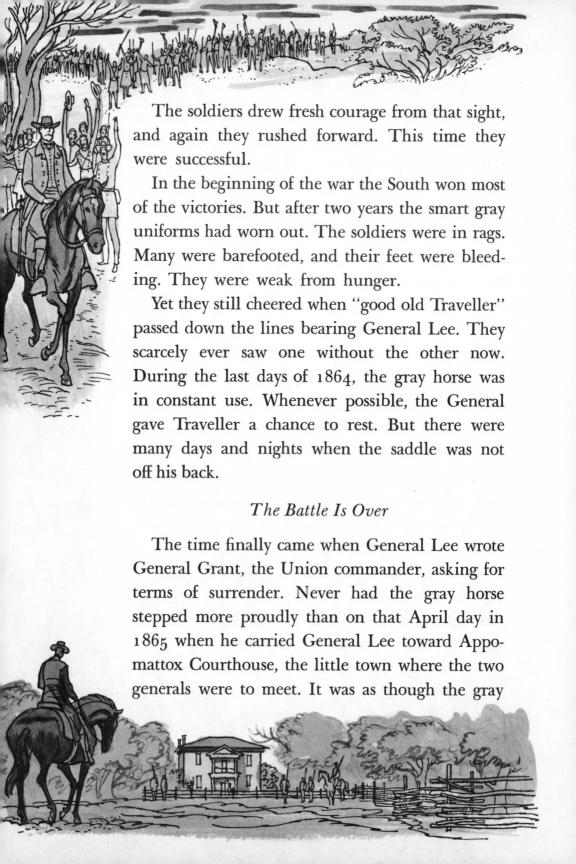

The soldiers drew fresh courage from that sight, and again they rushed forward. This time they were successful.

In the beginning of the war the South won most of the victories. But after two years the smart gray uniforms had worn out. The soldiers were in rags. Many were barefooted, and their feet were bleeding. They were weak from hunger.

Yet they still cheered when "good old Traveller" passed down the lines bearing General Lee. They scarcely ever saw one without the other now. During the last days of 1864, the gray horse was in constant use. Whenever possible, the General gave Traveller a chance to rest. But there were many days and nights when the saddle was not off his back.

The Battle Is Over

The time finally came when General Lee wrote General Grant, the Union commander, asking for terms of surrender. Never had the gray horse stepped more proudly than on that April day in 1865 when he carried General Lee toward Appomattox Courthouse, the little town where the two generals were to meet. It was as though the gray horse realized that his master was as great in defeat as he had been in victory.

Afterward, Traveller must have wondered at the strange scenes which took place. Men in tattered gray crowded around the horse and his rider. They tried to cheer, but the cheers ended in sobs. Some of them seemed to gain a little comfort from stroking Traveller's mane.

"Are we surrendered?" they asked.

The General nodded. "I have done the best I could. My heart is too full to say more."

The gray horse turned his head, as though in surprise. He whinnied softly.

After the war, General Lee became president of Washington College, in Lexington, Virginia. In Lexington the master and his horse had five peaceful years together. Every day they would go for a ride over the hilly roads.

The time came when the General could no longer take his daily ride. Sometimes he would gaze at the horse, his thoughts going back to the long marches, the cold nights and the bitter days, the noise and smoke of battle.

Then Traveller would whinny softly and nuzzle his master's shoulder. He, too, seemed to be remembering.

Breakfast with Buffalo Bill

Carol Ryrie Brink

*Bill Cody was a daredevil rider, one
of the youngest of the boys who rode for
the Pony Express. He was also a crack
shot. He earned his nickname, Buffalo
Bill, by killing thousands of buffaloes
to provide meat for railway workers.
Later, he became famous all over the
United States and Europe as manager
of the "Wild West Show." In this show,
cowboys, Indians, and western ponies
acted out the dangerous life of the
pioneer on the Great Plains.*

About ten minutes to four, in that darkest time
before the dawn, the first whistle of the *Wild West*
train sounded down the valley. Ardeth stirred in her
bed. Then a shower of pebbles struck her window
and brought her wide awake.

"Hey, there!" a voice called from below.

Ardeth ran to the window. Below on the lawn
were the shadowy forms of Martin and Henry
Dawlish.

"Hurry up!" hissed Martin. "It's nearly in. We'll miss the fun."

Ardeth flung on her clothes, shivering with excitement. In a moment she was hurrying down the dark street between Martin and Henry. The whistle of the *Wild West* train shrieked twice from the other side of town.

"We shook hands with Buffalo Bill last year in Montana," said Henry.

Ardeth had heard this several times before, but it always thrilled her. "Do you think he'll remember you?" she asked.

"I'll bet he will," said Henry.

When they reached the station, they watched the big work horses pulling the heavy, creaking wagons to the meadow where circuses always pitched their tents. Cowboys and Indians were driving oxen and leading rearing ponies. Indian tepees were being pitched in the field, and the enormous show tent was going up to the sound of shouts and grunts.

"Let's go and watch the cowboys have their breakfast," said Martin.

"Breakfast?" asked Ardeth. "Do they eat?"

"Sure. You can't move shows and do trick riding, and shooting, and bronco-busting without food, you know," said Martin.

The first tent to be completely set up was the dining tent. In a few moments the three stood by the open flap of the tent watching the cooks in their greasy white caps and aprons making breakfast. To her delight, Ardeth saw that they fried their ham and flipped their pancakes right on the tops of the stoves.

The *Wild West* people came in as they found time and sat down at bare wooden tables. It was like a picnic every day. There was a girl there in divided skirt and cowboy hat who might have been Annie Oakley, the sure-fire shot, herself. There were Indians, too, eating ham and eggs as peacefully as the cowboys. Just opposite the children sat a cowboy with a purple shirt and a ten-gallon hat. He was reading a paper-covered book called *The Life and Death of Jesse James, the Outlaw.*

Martin sniffed the good smell of frying ham and bacon. "I sure would like some breakfast," he said, "but I can't spare the time to go home."

"Oh, no," said Ardeth. "Let's not go home!"

Hard-Headed Henry

Just then Henry let out a whoop of delight and began to run.

"Buffalo Bill!" he yelled.

Across the meadow from the main tent cantered a white horse carrying a very erect rider with long white hair beneath his wide-brimmed hat. Colonel William Cody, the Indian fighter, the buffalo killer, the scout, was riding in to get his breakfast.

"It's Buffalo Bill!" said Martin. "It sure is!"

Henry ran on, his arms spread wide, shouting: "Buffalo Bill, you 'member me? I shook hands with you last year in Mon—"

The horse was coming faster than Henry had realized. Frightened by a blowing paper, it swerved suddenly and knocked him down. He rolled over and over on the dusty grass, and lay still.

Ardeth screamed, and Martin began to run. The old scout reined in his horse and cantered back. A little crowd gathered.

For a moment Henry lay quiet, his face white. "Henry!" called Martin. "Henry! Henry!"

Then Henry sat up, shaking his head, "—last year in Montana," he finished.

Buffalo Bill sprang off his horse and bent over him. "Well, now, young feller, you kind of ran amuck, didn't you?" he said.

"He was so glad to see you," explained Martin to Buffalo Bill. "Once he got his head caught in a cider press, but it didn't hurt him. Mama says he's got the Dawlish skull—you can't crack it."

"He'd make a good Indian fighter," said the old scout.

"You bet I would!" said Henry.

"Can you stand up?" asked the Colonel. "No bones broken?"

Henry stood up and dusted himself off. "I reckon I'm all here," he said.

"What's all this about Montana?"

"Martin and I shook your hand then. Don't you remember?"

"Well, I'm an old man, now, Bud. My memory's not what it used to be."

"I told you he wouldn't remember," said Martin.

"Oh, gee!" said Henry. "I had on my new straw hat, too."

"Well, no wonder!" said the Colonel. "How was I to know you without your hat? I've shook thousands of boys' hands since last summer. Had your breakfast?"

"No, sir, and we've been up since four."

"Come along, then. We'll see what we can do."

Ham and Eggs for Four!

Ardeth had an awful pang of fear. They were going off without her! She gave a little gasp, and Martin turned around and remembered her.

"This is Ardeth," he said politely. "She's never had the pleasure of shaking your hand."

"Petticoats, eh?" said the Colonel.

"She's all right," said Henry loyally. "She has a pony, and she knows how to ride it."

"That's different then. Shake hands, my girl."

Ardeth felt her hand being gripped hard by the very hand which had slain so many buffaloes. In a daze of delight, she followed along to the dining tent.

Buffalo Bill ranged them along one of the wooden benches and banged on the bare wooden table.

"Ham and eggs!" he shouted. "For Buffalo Bill and guests!"

The cooks ran about with a new burst of speed. "Coming up, Colonel!" they cried.

In a few moments they were all talking like old friends. Martin and Henry were telling Colonel Cody how they meant to be Indian fighters, too. Ardeth was describing her pony so that he sounded more like a fleet Indian hunter than a fat Shetland pony.

As for the food, ham and eggs and buckwheat cakes had never tasted better. This was the meal of a lifetime!

Glossary

This glossary, or small dictionary, contains the more unusual words from the stories in this book. Usually, only the meaning is given that fits the word the first time it is used. The "key" at the bottom of the pages helps to show how each word is pronounced. The regular dictionary should be used to learn meanings of other words you find difficult, or other meanings for the words given here.

A

ac·com'pa·ny (à·kŭm'pà·nĭ). To go with.

ac·com'plish (à·kŏm'plĭsh). To do.

ac·knowl'edge (ăk·nŏl'ĕj). To show that something has been received or noticed.

a·do'be (à·dō'bĭ). Brick dried in the sun instead of in an oven.

air (âr). Melody, tune.

al'ma·nac (ôl'mà·năk). Calendar in book form with facts about sunrise and sunset, tides, and other useful information.

am'ber (ăm'bẽr). Golden-yellow material obtained from trees and often used for beads and other ornaments.

and'i·ron (ănd'ī'ẽrn). Iron holder for logs in a fireplace.

a·pol'o·gy (à·pŏl'ô·jĭ). Statement that one is sorry for doing something wrong.

ap·pren'tice (à·prĕn'tĭs). One who is learning a trade under a skilled worker.

ar'bor (är'bẽr). Wooden frame on which vines grow.

arch (ärch). To stretch up and forward in a curve.

ar·roy'o (à·roi'ō). Stream bed with steep sides, often dry in summer.

as·ton'ish (ăs·tŏn'ĭsh). To surprise greatly, amaze.

at·tach' (à·tăch'). To join or fasten one thing to another.

at'ti·tude (ăt'tĭ·tūd). Point of view, feeling.

B

bal'lad (băl'ăd). Song or poem of adventure.

be·wil'der (bê·wĭl'dẽr). To puzzle, confuse.

bleat (blēt). To make a cry like that of a sheep or a goat.

bliz'zard (blĭz'zẽrd). Long, heavy snowstorm with strong winds.

bob'bin (bŏb'ĭn). Spool for yarn on a spinning wheel.

bolt (bōlt). To run, move quickly.

bo'nus (bō'nŭs). Extra pay.

both'er (bŏth'ẽr). To annoy or trouble or disturb.

Brah'man (brä'măn). Indian Hindu of the highest social group.

bram'ble (brăm'b'l). Prickly bush, such as a blackberry bush.

breed (brēd). Kind or variety of animals.

bri'ar patch (brī'ẽr păch). Piece of ground on which prickly bushes are growing.

ā, āte; à, furnàce; ă, ăt; ạ, ạppear; â, câre; ä, cär; à, pàss; ȧ, sofȧ; ē, bē; ê, bêgin; ĕ, lĕt; ê, silênt; ē, watēr; ê, hêre; ī, hīde; ĭ, hĭd; ĭ, cabĭn; ō, hōpe; ộ, ộmit; ŏ, hŏp; ô, cŏntain; ô, ôr; ộ, sộft; ōō, fōōd; ŏŏ, fŏŏt; oi, oil; ou, out; ū, ūse; ŭ, ŭnite; ŭ, ŭs; ụ, circụs; û, fûr; tụ, natụre; dụ, verdụre; th, thin; th, than.

brim (brĭm). Flat rim of a hat.

brisk (brĭsk). Lively.

broil′er (broil′ẽr). Young, tender chicken.

broth (brôth). Thin soup of a clear, brown color.

budge (bŭj). To move.

bun′dle (bŭn′d’l). To tie up in a bunch or a package.

bus′tle (bŭs″l). To move about busily or noisily.

C

cal′i·co (kăl′ĭ·kō). Cotton cloth with small, bright-colored flowers in it; spotted (when describing a cat or a horse).

can′ter (kăn′tẽr). To gallop gently.

can′vas (kăn′vȧs). Strong cloth used for tents, sails, etc.

card′ing comb (kärd′ĭng kōm). Comb for cleaning and untangling wool before making yarn.

car′go (kär′gō). Load carried by a ship.

car′riage (kăr′ĭj). Manner of holding one's head and body.

ca·vort′ (kȧ·vôrt′). To move around playfully or excitedly, to prance.

chant (chȧnt). To say something over and over in the same tone of voice.

charge (chärj). To attack.

chest′nut (chĕs′nŭt). Short name for a chestnut-colored horse.

chores (chōrz). Little jobs that must be done daily about the house or farm.

chub′by (chŭb′ĭ). Plump, round.

chuck′le (chŭk″l). To laugh quietly or to oneself.

clasp (klȧsp). To hold. (To *clasp hands* is to hold one hand with the other.)

clat′ter (klăt′ẽr). To move with a rattling sound.

clue (kloō). A hint or a fact that may help one to solve a mystery.

com·pan′ion (kŏm·păn′yŭn). Friend, person who does something with you.

con·cerned′ (kŏn·sûrnd′). Worried, anxious.

con·cern′ing (kŏn·sûr′nĭng). About.

con′quest (kŏng′kwĕst). Victory.

con′science (kŏn′shĕns). Understanding of the difference between right and wrong.

con·sent′ (kŏn·sĕnt′). To agree.

con·tent′ (kŏn·tĕnt′). Satisfied, pleased.

cor·ral′ (kŏ·räl′). Large pen for horses or cattle.

coun′cil·man (koun′sĭl·măn). Man who helps make the laws of a city.

coy′ote (kī′ōt). Small wolf.

crack (krăk). Very good, first-class.

crane (krān). Swinging metal arm that holds a kettle over a fire.

crate (krāt). Box made of narrow boards with spaces between them.

creak (krēk). Long, sharp squeak.

cre·a′tion (krḗ·ā′shŭn). Act of making something.

crew (kroō). Group of people working together.

crock (krŏk). Jar or pot.

cro′cus (krō′kŭs). Early spring flower.

crouch (krouch). To bend low.

ā, āte; ȧ, furnȧce; ă, ăt; ȧ, ăppear; â, câre; ä, cär; ȧ, pȧss; ȧ, sofȧ; ē, bē; ḗ, bḗgin; ĕ, lĕt; ẽ, silẽnt; ẽ, watẽr; ẹ, hẹre; ī, hīde; ĭ, hĭd; ĭ, cabĭn; ō, hōpe;

crown (kroun). English coin worth about $.70.

crum′ple (krŭm′p′l). To squeeze into wrinkles or uneven folds.

crys′tal (krĭs′tăl). Glass.

D

daw′dle (dô′d′l). To be very slow in doing anything.

dawn (dôn). First light of day.

dea′con (dē′kŭn). Church officer who helps the minister or priest.

dec′o·rous (dĕk′ō·rŭs). Well-behaved.

del′i·cate (dĕl′ĭ·kĭt). Pleasing because of being fine or sensitive.

del′i·ca·tes′sen (dĕl′ĭ·kă·tĕs′ĕn). Store which sells fine foods, especially meats that are already cooked.

delve (dĕlv). To dig.

de·press′ (dė·prĕs′). To make sad.

de·sign′ (dė·zīn′). Figure or pattern made by an artist.

de·spair′ (dė·spâr′). Hopelessness.

de·ter′mined (dė·tûr′mĭnd). Decided, having a settled point of view.

dic′tate (dĭk′tāt). To tell or say something for someone else to write down.

dis′ad·van′tage (dĭs′ăd·văn′tĭj). Drawback, something that acts as a hindrance.

dis·ap·pear′ (dĭs′ă·pēr′). To go out of sight.

dis·grace′ (dĭs·grās′). To bring shame or dishonor to.

dis′mal (dĭz′măl). Sad, gloomy.

dor′mouse′ (dôr′mous′). Small animal something like a squirrel.

down′cast′ (doun′kȧst′). Sad.

droop (drōōp). To hang down, sag.

drum′stick′ (drŭm′stĭk′). The leg of a chicken or turkey as an article of food.

dunk (dŭngk). To dip.

dye (dī). To color.

E

ear′nest (ûr′nĕst). Serious, sincere.

eaves (ēvz). Overhanging edges of roof.

el′e·gant (ĕl′ė·gănt). Correct or proper in dress and manners.

em·bar′rass (ĕm·băr′ăs). To upset someone's feelings, make him feel shame.

em′ber (ĕm′bēr). Red-hot coal.

e·mer′gen·cy (ė·mûr′jĕn·sĭ). Unexpected happening which must be attended to at once.

e·nor′mous (ė·nôr′mŭs). Huge.

e·rect′ (ė·rĕkt′). Straight up, not leaning or slouching.

ex·ag′ger·ate (ĕg·zăj′ĕr·āt). To enlarge upon the truth, overstate, magnify.

F

fab′ric (făb′rĭk). Cloth.

fal′ter (fôl′tēr). To hesitate or become uncertain in purpose or action.

fas′ci·nate (făs′ĭ·nāt). To hold a person's interest.

fee′ble (fē′b′l). Weak.

fell (fĕl). To cut down.

fe·ro′cious (fė·rō′shŭs). Very fierce.

fer′ry (fĕr′ĭ). To carry over a river in a boat.

fetch (fĕch). To go and get.

ô̱, ômit; ŏ, hŏp; ǒ, cŏntain; ô, ôr; ộ, sôft; ōō, fōod; ŏŏ, fŏot; oi, oil; ou, out; ū, ūse; ụ, ụnite; ŭ, ŭs; ụ̆, circŭs; û, fûr; tụ̱, natụ̱re; dụ̱, verdụ̱re; th, thin; t̶h̶, t̶h̶an.

fil′ter (fĭl′tēr). To pass through a screen of some kind, sift through.

fir (fûr). Kind of pine tree.

five-pound note (fīv·pound nōt). English paper money now worth about $14.

flap′jack′ (flăp′jăk′). Pancake.

flat′i′ron (flăt′ī′ẽrn). Iron for pressing clothes, usually one heated on a stove.

fleet (flēt). Swift, fast-moving.

floun′der (floun′dẽr). To move ahead or about in a clumsy way.

flut′ed (flōōt′ĕd). Grooved, channeled.

for′eign (fŏr′ĭn). Of another country.

fowl (foul). Large bird.

freak′i·est (frēk′ĭ·ĕst). Oddest.

fret (frĕt). To worry.

fur′row (fûr′ō). Groove or channel made by a plow.

fu′ry (fū′rĭ). Fierceness, violence.

G

gait (gāt). Manner of walking or running.

gar′gle (gär′g′l). To wash out one's mouth with water or medicine.

gasp (gȧsp). To speak with short bursts of breath.

gilt (gĭlt). Golden.

girth (gûrth). Band that goes around a horse's middle and holds the saddle in place.

gleam′ing (glēm′ĭng). Flashing, shining.

glimpse (glĭmps). To catch sight of for only a moment.

glis′ten (glĭs″n). To shine or sparkle.

gnarled (närld). Twisted, full of knots.

gourd (gōrd). Bottle made from a dried fruit, such as a squash.

grim′ly (grĭm′lĭ). Fiercely, sternly.

grits (grĭts). Coarse cooked cereal.

groove (grōōv). Long slit or channel.

grub (grŭb). To dig.

grudge (grŭj). To envy.

guilt′y (gĭl′tĭ). Deserving blame, being at fault.

gui·tar′ (gĭ·tär′). Musical instrument played with the fingers.

gun′ny sack (gŭn′nĭ săk). Bag made of coarse, brown fiber.

gur′gle (gûr′g′l). To sound like water being poured out of a bottle.

H

hack (hăk). To chop in a crude or unskilled way.

haft (hȧft). Handle.

hal′ter (hôl′tẽr). Strap for leading or tying a horse.

har·poon′ (här·pōōn′). Spear for catching whales.

haunch (hônch). Hip.

hearth (härth). Brick or stone floor in front of a fireplace.

heart′-rend′ing (härt′ rĕnd′ĭng). Very sad, heartbreaking.

heave (hēv). To rise and fall rapidly time after time, as the chest of a person who is panting.

hew (hū). To chop.

hoarse (hōrs). Unpleasant in sound, like the voice of a person who has a cold.

hor′rid (hŏr′ĭd). Very unpleasant.

ā, āte; ȧ, furnȧce; ă, ăt; ₐ̆, ₐ̆ppear; â, câre; ä, cär; ȧ, pȧss; ₐ̇, sofȧ; ē, bē; ė̄, bḗgin; ĕ, lĕt; ₑ̆, silₑ̆nt; ẽ, watẽr; ē̦, hē̦re; ī, hīde; ĭ, hĭd; ₐ̆, cabₐ̆n; ō, hōpe;

hor′ri·fy (hŏr′ĭ·fī). To make one very troubled or fearful.

hus′tle (hŭs″l). To move quickly and energetically.

I

id′i·ot (ĭd′ĭ·ŭt). Foolish person.

i′dle (ī′d′l). To waste time.

im·port′ (ĭm·pōrt′). To bring in from another country.

In′di·an a′gen·cy (ĭn′dĭ·ăn ā′jĕn·sĭ). Government office that helps Indians.

in·sist′ (ĭn·sĭst′). To decide on something and refuse to change.

in·spire′ (ĭn·spīr′). To encourage, fill with confidence.

in·tent′ [on] (ĭn·tĕnt′). Interested in.

in·vent′ (ĭn·vĕnt′). To do or make for the first time; to discover through thought and experiment.

J

jack′straws′ (jăk′strôz′). Game played with strips (straws) of wood or bone.

jeer (jēr). To make fun of in an unkind way.

jog (jŏg). To trot slowly.

jum′ble (jŭm′b′l). To mix up, disarrange.

jum′bles (jŭm′b′lz). Small, thin cookies.

ju′ni·per (jōō′nĭ·pĕr). Variety of evergreen tree.

L

la′bel (lā′bĕl). To fasten a name tag to something.

lap (lăp). To splash gently against.

lawn (lôn). Kind of thin cotton or linen cloth.

lep′re·chaun (lĕp′rĕ·kôn). Fairy who appears as a little old man.

limp (lĭmp). Weak, lacking strength.

liv′er·y sta′ble (lĭv′ẽr·ĭ stā′b′l). Building where horses that may be hired are kept.

lo′co (lō′cō). Crazy (Spanish).

loft (lôft). Upper room of a barn, usually used to store hay.

loll′ing (lŏl′ĭng). Hanging loosely.

loy′al·ly (loi′ăl·lĭ). In support of or with faithfulness toward a friend.

loz′enge (lŏz′ĕnj). Small, flat, round candy.

lum′ber (lŭm′bẽr). To move or walk heavily or clumsily.

M

Mack′i·naw (măk′ĭ·nô). Short, heavy coat.

mag·nif′i·cent (măg·nĭf′ĭ·sĕnt). Grand, splendid.

man′age (măn′ĭj). To control, to guide the behavior of.

man′tel·piece′ (măn′t′l·pēs′). Shelf over a fireplace.

mare (mâr). Female horse.

mar′i·o·nette′ (măr′ĭ·ȯ·nĕt′). Doll moved by strings or by hand; puppet.

mar′vel·ous (mär′vĕl·ŭs). Wonderful.

me′sa (mā′så). Flat-topped hill common in the southwestern United States.

me·tal′lic (mė·tăl′ĭk). Made of metal.

mill′er (mĭl′ẽr). Person who makes flour.

mil′li·ner (mĭl′ĭ·nẽr). Person who makes or sells women's hats.

mince (mĭns). Chopped food.

mir′a·cle (mĭr′å·k′l). Very strange and wonderful happening.

ȯ, ȯmit; ŏ, hŏp; ŏ, cŏntain; ô, ôr; ô, sȯft; ōō, fōōd; ŏŏ, fŏŏt; oi, oil; ou, out; ū, ūse; û, ûnite; ŭ, ŭs; ŭ, circŭs; û, fûr; tŭ, natŭre; dŭ, verdŭre; th, thin; ~~th~~, ~~th~~an.

muf'fin (mŭf'ĭn). A quick bread baked in a small round pan.

muss (mŭs). To put in disorder, disarrange.

mut'ter (mŭt'ẽr). To speak in a low, unclear voice.

mut'ton (mŭt"n). Meat from a sheep.

N

nes'tle (nĕs"l). To sit close and snug.

nib'ble (nĭb"l). To eat in very small bites.

nick'er (nĭk'ẽr). To neigh.

nip (nĭp). To cause to ache with cold.

nought (nôt). Nothing.

nuz'zle (nŭz"l). To push or rub affectionately with the nose.

O

ob'ject (ŏb'jĕkt). Thing.

o·blig'ing (ȯ·blīj'ĭng). Helpful.

o'gre (ō'gẽr). Ugly giant.

o·rig'i·nal (ȯ·rĭj'ĭ·năl). First.

P

pad'lock' (păd'lŏk'). Removable lock with a hinged loop.

pang (păng). Sudden short sharp pain.

pan'nier bas'kets (păn'yẽr bȧs'kĕts). Large baskets carried one on each side of a horse's back.

pars'ley (pärs'lĭ). Vegetable with green, curly leaves used to decorate platters of food.

par·tic'u·lar (pẽr·tĭk'ů·lẽr). Certain, separate.

pas'sion (păsh'ŭn). Great anger.

pe·cul'iar (pė·kūl'yẽr). Odd.

peer (pẽr). To look closely.

pet'ri·fy (pĕt'rĭ·fī). To become as hard as stone.

pew'ter (pū'tẽr). Made of lead and tin.

pic'co·lo (pĭk'ȯ·lō). Musical instrument similar to a fife or a flute.

pick'et (pĭk'ĕt). Up-and-down fence boards, pointed on top.

pin'na·cle (pĭn'ȧ·k'l). Pointed top.

pin'to (pĭn'tō). Spotted.

pin'yon (pĭn'yŭn). Pine of western North America.

pip'pin (pĭp'ĭn). Kind of apple.

pitch (pĭch). To fix firmly in the ground, set up.

plague (plāg). Disease.

pleat (plēt). To fold or braid.

pli'a·ble (plī'ȧ·b'l). Easily bent.

po'ny ex·press' (pō'nĭ ĕks·prĕs'). System of carrying mail by fast ponies or horses.

pop'lar (pŏp'lẽr). Kind of tree.

por'ridge (pŏr'ĭj). Boiled cereal.

pos·sess' (pŏ·zĕs'). To own.

pot'ter·y (pŏt'ẽr·ĭ). Clay dishes.

pouch (pouch). Small bag.

prai'rie (prâr'ĭ). Treeless, grassy plain.

pranc'ing (prȧns'ĭng). Moving gaily or proudly, with springing steps.

pre'cious (prĕsh'ŭs). Very valuable.

pre·dic'a·ment (prė·dĭk'ȧ·mĕnt). Trouble, bad condition or situation.

pre·serve' (prė·zûrv'). To protect.

press (prĕs). Machine for pressing or squeezing.

ā, āte; ȧ, furnȧce; ă, ăt; ạ, ạppear; â, câre; ä, cär; ȧ, pȧss; ȧ, sofȧ; ē, bē; ė, bėgin; ĕ, lĕt; ę, silęnt; ẽ, watẽr; ē, hēre; ī, hīde; ĭ, hĭd; ĭ, cabĭn; ō, hōpe;

prime min′is·ter (prīm mĭn′ĭs·tẽr). Title of the chief officer in many governments.

prob′a·bly (prŏb′ȧ·blĭ). Very likely.

pro·ces′sion (prō̍·sĕsh′ŭn). Parade.

prod (prŏd). Push.

prop (prŏp). To hold up or keep from falling.

prop′er·ty (prŏp′ẽr·tĭ). Anything that a person owns.

pueb′lo (pwĕb′lō). Indian village of apartment-like adobe buildings in Arizona or New Mexico.

puf′fin (pŭf′ĭn). Sea bird with a large bill.

pur′chase (pûr′chĭs). Act of buying something.

pyr′a·mid (pĭr′ȧ·mĭd). Anything with several triangular sides sloping up to a point.

Q

quay (kē). Dock.

quince (kwĭns). A fruit used for jelly.

quiv′er (kwĭv′ẽr). Shiver.

R

range (rānj). Open land where cattle feed; also, a row of mountains.

ran′gy (rān′jĭ). Long-legged and thin.

ranks (răngks). Lines or companies of ordinary soldiers.

rasp (rasp). Harsh, unpleasant sound.

re′al·ize (rē′ăl·īz). To understand.

realm (rĕlm). Kingdom.

reap′er (rēp′ẽr). Harvester of grain.

rear (rēr). To rise up on the hind legs.

re′as·sure′ (rē′ă·sho͝or′). To free from fear.

rec′og·nize (rĕk′ŏg·nīz). To know again, to remember a person or thing when he or it is seen at a later time.

re·joice′ (rē̍·jois′). To feel great joy.

re·luc′tant (rē̍·lŭk′tănt). Unwilling, not eager.

re·prove′ (rē̍·pro͞ov′). To scold.

ridge (rĭj). High land sloping down on two sides.

rou·tine′ (ro͞o·tēn′). Acts repeated by habit.

ruf′fle (rŭf″l). Folded trimmings on a dress.

rum′ble (rŭm′b′l). To make a low, rolling sound like distant thunder.

rum′mage (rŭm′ĭj). To search carefully.

run′ci·ble spoon (rŭn′sĭ·b′l spo͞on). Three-tined fork curved like a spoon.

rush (rŭsh). A swamp plant.

rus′set (rŭs′ĕt). Apple of a yellowish-brown color.

S

sage (sāj). Low bush (also called *sagebrush*) of the western plains.

saun′ter (sôn′tẽr). To walk slowly.

scal′lop (skŏl′ŭp). To make a wavy edge on anything.

scamp (skămp). Rascal, good-for-nothing person.

scant (skănt). Barely enough.

scent (sĕnt). Odor, or smell, left by an animal.

scorn′ful (skôrn′fo͝ol). Feeling dislike for something not worth respect.

ō̍, ō̍mit; ŏ, hŏp; ŏ, cŏntain; ô, ôr; ŏ̂, sŏ̂ft; o͞o, fo͞od; o͝o, fo͝ot; oi, oil; ou, out; ū, ūse: ū̍, ū̍nite; ŭ, ŭs; ŭ, circŭs; û, fûr; tū, natūre; dū, verdūre; th, thin; th, than.

scram'ble (skrăm'b'l). To climb by using hands and knees.

scur'ry (skûr'ĭ). To hurry.

sen'ti·men'tal (sĕn'tĭ·mĕn'tăl). Soft-hearted.

se·vere' (sė·vēr'). Unkind, harsh.

shan'ty (shăn'tĭ). Small, poor house; hut.

shear (shēr). To cut off with scissors, especially wool from a sheep.

shil'ling (shĭl'ĭng). English silver coin worth 14 cents.

shrewd (shrōōd). Sharp-witted, keen.

shrill (shrĭl). Having a sharp, high-pitched sound.

singe (sĭnj). To burn the end or outside of.

sin'gle [out] (sĭn'g'l). To choose one person or thing out of a group.

site (sīt). A place where something such as a house is, was, or will be.

slack (slăk). Loose, not tight.

slant'wise' (slànt'wīz'). Sloping, not straight up and down.

slash'ing (slăsh'ĭng). Branches left after trees have been cut into logs.

sledge ham'mer (slĕj hăm'ēr). Large heavy hammer.

slen'der (slĕn'dēr). Thin, slim.

smart (smärt). To feel a sharp or stinging pain.

smith (smĭth). Person, such as a blacksmith, who works with metals.

smith'y (smĭth'ĭ). A smith's workshop.

snatch (snăch). To seize or grab quickly.

snort (snôrt). To speak suddenly or explosively and with displeasure.

soar (sōr). To fly upward.

sol'emn (sŏl'ĕm). Grave, thoughtful.

sort (sôrt). To separate by kind.

sour'dough' (sour'dō'). Yeasty matter which makes bread light and soft.

spare (spâr). To show mercy to.

spell'bound' (spĕl'bound'). Charmed, fascinated.

splin'ter (splĭn'tēr). Long, thin piece; sliver.

squat (skwŏt). To sit on one's heels.

squirm (skwûrm). To wiggle, often in discomfort.

stag'ger (stăg'ēr). To walk unevenly, as if about to fall.

stam'mer (stăm'ēr). To speak in a jerky way; to stutter.

sta'tion (stā'shŭn). Building or office that is the headquarters of certain groups, such as policemen or firemen.

stir'rup (stĭr'ŭp). Looped support for the rider's foot, hung from a saddle.

strew (strōō). To place here and there; to scatter.

stride (strīd). To walk rapidly, with long steps.

strut (strŭt). To walk proudly.

stur'dy (stûr'dĭ). Strong.

surge (sûrj). To rush or push forward with a wavelike motion.

swarm (swôrm). To crowd around, as bees and other insects do.

swerve (swûrv). To turn aside.

T

tar'ry (tăr'ĭ). To be slow in acting; to delay.

ā, āte; å, furnåce; ă, ăt; ȧ, ȧppear; â, câre; ä, cär; à, pàss; ȧ, sofȧ; ē, bē;
ė, bėgin; ĕ, lĕt; ẽ, silẽnt; ẽ, watẽr; ḛ, ḛere; ī, hīde; ĭ, hĭd; ɩ, cabɩn; ō, hōpe;

tat′tered (tăt′ẽrd). Ragged.

taw′ny (tô′nĭ). Yellowish-brown.

tel′e·scope (tĕl′ē·skōp). Spyglass, instrument for making things far away look nearer and larger.

terms (tûrmz). Points for agreement.

ter′ri·fy (tĕr′ĭ·fī). To frighten very much.

thatch (thăch). To cover with a roof of straw or reeds.

thong (thŏng). Narrow strip of leather.

threat (thrĕt). Statement of intention to hurt someone in some way.

thrush (thrŭsh). Kind of songbird.

thwack (thwăk). To hit, strike.

tide (tīd). Twice-daily rise and fall of the surface level of the ocean.

ti′dy (tī′dĭ). To make neater.

tongs (tŏngz). Tool for lifting things. Tongs usually work like scissors.

tor′rent (tŏr′ĕnt). Flood.

tot′ter (tŏt′ẽr). To shake or sway as if about to fall.

trea′ty (trē′tĭ). Agreement.

trick′le (trĭk″l). To flow in a tiny stream.

twi′light′ (twī′līt′). Light from the sky after sunset.

twirl (twûrl). To whirl, turn rapidly.

twitch (twĭch). To move in a jerky way.

U

un·bear′a·ble (ŭn·bâr′à·b′l). More than one can stand.

u′ni·verse (ū′nĭ·vûrs). The whole world, including the stars and planets.

up′shot′ (ŭp′shŏt′). Result, end.

urge (ûrj). To argue earnestly for something, try to persuade.

urn (ûrn). A type of vase that usually narrows from the top down, then widens out into a flat base.

V

vast (vȧst). Wide, very large.

ven′i·son (vĕn′ĭ·z′n). Deer meat.

ven′ture (vĕn′t̯u̯r). To dare, take a chance.

W

wad′dle (wŏd″l). To walk with short steps, swinging from side to side awkwardly.

wa′ter cress (wô′tẽr krĕs). Salad plant that grows in water.

wa′ver (wā′vẽr). To grow bright and then dim time after time; to flicker.

wedge (wĕj). Tool that is thick on one end but has a thin edge on the other, somewhat like a chisel. It is used for splitting wood or stone or for driving and holding things apart.

whim′per (hwĭm′pẽr). To cry in low, broken tones.

whin′ny (hwĭn′ĭ). To neigh gently.

whisk (hwĭsk). To move quickly.

whoop (hōōp). Loud cry or shout.

wick (wĭk). The part of an oil lamp or candle that is lighted.

wil′der·ness (wĭl′dẽr·nĕs). Wild place where nobody lives.

wil′ly-nil′ly (wĭl′ĭ·nĭl′ĭ). Whether one likes it or not.

ō, ōmit; ŏ, hŏp; ǒ, cǒntain; ô, ôr; ộ, sộft; ōō, fōōd; ŏŏ, fŏŏt; oi, oil; ou, out; ū, ūse; u̇, u̇nite; ŭ, ŭs; ů, circůs; û, fûr; t̯u̯, nat̯u̯re; d̯u̯, verd̯u̯re; th, thin; t̶h̶, t̶h̶a̶n̶.

ACKNOWLEDGMENTS

For their courteous permission to use the following selections in this book, we wish to express our gratitude and appreciation to the following authors, publishers, and periodicals:

Ellis Credle: "The Bear and the Wildcat" and "The Blizzard of '98," adapted from TALL TALES FROM THE HIGH HILLS, copyright 1946 by Story Parade, Inc. — Beatrice Curtis Brown: "Jonathan Bing" from JONATHAN BING AND OTHER VERSES, copyright 1936 by Beatrice Curtis Brown. — Richard W. Emery: "Billy Goats Chew" from *Child Life*, copyright 1936 by Rand McNally & Co. — Aileen Fisher: "Early Crocus," copyright 1951 by Wesleyan University. — Ethel Romig Fuller: "Wind Is a Cat" from WHITE PEAKS AND GREEN. — Florence Page Jaques: "There Once Was a Puffin" from *Child Life*. — Lenore M. Link: "Holding Hands" from *St. Nicholas*. Winifred Welles: "Skipping Along Alone"; by permission of the author's estate. — Abingdon-Cokesbury Press: "Cats for Kansas" by LeGrand, copyright 1948 by LeGrand-Henderson. — George T. Bye & Co.: "Sheep Shearing" from FARMER BOY by Laura Ingalls Wilder, copyright 1933 by Harper & Bros. — Coward-McCann, Inc.: "Kattor," adapted from THE STORY OF KATTOR by Georgia Travers, copyright 1939 by Flavia Gag and Georgia Travers. — Dodd, Mead & Company: "Town Moose" from HONK THE MOOSE by Phil Stong, copyright 1935 by Phil Stong. — Doubleday & Company, Inc.: "Mr. Murdle's Large Heart" from a STREET OF LITTLE SHOPS by Margery Bianco, copyright 1932 by Margery Williams Bianco; "A Trip to Lancaster Market" from HENNER'S LYDIA by Marguerite deAngeli, copyright 1936 by Marguerite deAngeli; "City Rain" and "The Animal Store" from TAXIS AND TOADSTOOLS by Rachel Field, copyright 1926 by Doubleday & Company, Inc.: "When Glory Went To Peddle Pine" from THE OTHER SIDE OF THE MOUNTAINS by May Justus, copyright 1931 by May Justus; and "Chi-wee and the Pinyon Nuts" from CHI-WEE by Grace Moon, copyright 1925 by Doubleday & Company, Inc. — The Society of Authors (London), Messrs. Methuen & Co., Ltd. (London), and Doubleday & Company, Inc.: "The Best Game the Fairies Play" from FAIRIES AND CHIMNEYS by Rose Fyleman, copyright 1920 by Doubleday & Company, Inc. — Harcourt, Brace and Company, Inc.: "The Fish Money" from PEACHTREE ISLAND by Mildred Lawrence, copyright 1948 by Harcourt, Brace and Company, Inc.; and "Judy Grows Up" from JUDY'S BABY by Sally Scott, copyright 1940 by Harcourt, Brace and Company, Inc. — Holiday House: "Building the Rockies" from OL' PAUL, THE MIGHTY LOGGER by Glen Rounds, copyright 1936 by Holiday House, Inc. — Henry Holt and Company, Inc.: "Miss T" and "Some One" from COLLECTED POEMS by Walter de la Mare, copyright 1920 by Henry Holt and Company, Inc., 1948 by Walter de la Mare; and "The Pasture" from COMPLETE POEMS BY ROBERT FROST, copyright 1930, 1949 by Henry Holt and Company, Inc. — Houghton Mifflin Company: "Comanche and the Fire" from WILL ROGERS, THE BOY ROPER by Donald and Beth Day, copyright 1950; "Daisies" and "Flying Kite" by Frank Dempster Sherman, from LITTLE FOLK LYRICS; "Brer Rabbit and the Tar Baby" from YANKEE DOODLE'S COUSINS by Anne Malcolmson, copyright 1941 by Anne Burnett Malcolmson; and from the same book "Febold Feboldson" (adapted by Anne Malcolmson from FEBOLD FEBOLDSON: TALL TALES FROM THE PLAINS by Paul R. Beath, The University of Nebraska Press). — Alfred A. Knopf, Inc.: "The Mystery of Egbert" from FREDDIE THE DETECTIVE by Walter R. Brooks, copyright 1932 by Walter R. Brooks. — Little, Brown & Company: "A Bird Came Down the Walk" from POEMS BY EMILY DICKINSON, edited by Martha Dickinson Bianchi and Alfred Leete Hampson, Little, Brown & Company; "Jippy and Jimmy" and "The Monkeys and the Crocodile" from TIRRA LIRRA by Laura E. Richards. — The Macmillan Company: "The Sea Gull" from PLUM DAFFY ADVENTURE by Elizabeth Coatsworth, copyright 1947; "The Isle Should Have a Pine Tree" from SUMMER GREEN by Elizabeth Coatsworth, copyright 1928; "Yet Gentle Will the Griffin Be" from JOHNNY APPLESEED AND OTHER POEMS by Vachel Lindsay, copyright 1930; and "The Falling Star" from STARS TONIGHT by Sara Teasdale, copyright 1930. — William Heinemann, Ltd. (London), and The Macmillan Company: "The Hairy Dog" from PILLICOCK HILL by Herbert Asquith. — Mrs. James Stephens (London), Macmillan & Co., Ltd. (London) and The Macmillan Company: "The White Window" from COLLECTED POEMS by James Stephens, copyright 1927. — William Morrow & Company, Inc.: "Any Old Junk Today?" from LITTLE EDDIE by Carolyn Haywood, copyright 1947 by William Morrow & Company, Inc. — Thomas Nelson & Sons, New York: "How the Little Old Woman Saved Her Last Match" from THE LITTLE OLD WOMAN WHO USED HER HEAD by Hope Newell, copyright 1935. — Arthur S. Pederson: "The Little Rose Tree" and "Roads" from POINTED PEOPLE by Rachel Field. — Row, Peterson & Company: "Boots and His Brothers" and "Gudbrand-on-the-Hillside" from EAST O' THE SUN AND WEST O' THE MOON by Gudrun Thorne-Thomson, copyright 1912 by Row, Peterson & Company. — Charles Scribner's Sons: "Trot Along, Pony" from THE OPEN DOOR by Marion Edey and Dorothy Grider, copyright 1949 by Marion Edey and Dorothy Grider. — Simon and Schuster, Inc.: "Kitten-in-a-Basket" from THE GIANT GOLDEN BOOK OF CAT STORIES by Elizabeth Coatsworth, copyright 1953 by Simon and Schuster, Inc. and Artists and Writers Guild, Inc. — Story Parade, Inc., for the following, copyright in the years indicated by Story Parade, Inc.: "The Lion" by Elizabeth Coatsworth (1946); "Whopper" by Nan Gilbert (1942); "Pino and Paint" by Dan Noonan (1948); and "The Enchanted Rabbit" by Robin Palmer (1951). — Cloyd Head: "Moving" by Eunice Tietjens, from *Child Life*. — The Viking Press, Inc., New York: "Lost in the Apple Cave" and "Betsy's New Hat" from CHILDREN OF THE HANDCRAFTS by Carolyn Sherwin Bailey, copyright 1935 by Carolyn Sherwin Bailey; "Serapina Takes Charge" from THE STORY OF SERAPINA by Anne H. White, copyright 1951 by Anne H. White; excerpts adapted from the original texts by permission of the publisher; and "The Hens" and "The Circus" from UNDER THE TREE by Elizabeth Madox Roberts, copyright 1922 by B. W. Huebsch, Inc., 1950 by Ivor S. Roberts.